THE SCIENCE
AND THE MYSTERY
OF THE CAT

The tabby markings of Rasputin of Cleveland, Ohio, reveal his wild cat ancestry, but his short ears might have puzzled the ancient Egyptians.

THE SCIENCE
AND THE MYSTERY
OF THE CAT

ITS EVOLUTIONARY STATUS, ANTIQUITY
AS A PET, BODY, BRAIN, BEHAVIOR,
SO-CALLED "OCCULT POWERS,"
AND ITS EFFECT ON PEOPLE

By

Ida M. Mellen

Zoölogist, author of "A Practical Cat Book,"
Honorary Vice-President of the Allied Cat Lovers, Inc.

CHARLES SCRIBNER'S SONS · NEW YORK
CHARLES SCRIBNER'S SONS · LTD · LONDON
1949

FOREWORD

CATS, like fishes, are so common everywhere that nobody knows very much about them, and no work concerning cats, though it occupy a lifetime, can safely be regarded as final in every detail.

The cat, like those reflective Eastern peoples among whom it has lived for thousands of years, suggests the intangible, and is the most difficult animal in the world about which to make accurate observations or to procure reliable information. That prince of observers, Charles Darwin himself, admitted that he had erred in some of his conclusions respecting cats!

The animal is called mysterious, inscrutable and occult, and its psychology is but imperfectly understood; yet many of its mysterious manifestations have a physical basis, such as foretelling the weather and knowing that certain persons are approaching when the human ear detects no sound.

Since my own studies have been limited to a period of two dozen years, it has been necessary to label some points "unknown"; but this volume contains more than one hundred new facts, as well as entire chapters covering aspects of the cat not heretofore noticed, and it necessarily disproves some common beliefs regarding the elusive feline.

Many people in both eastern and western hemispheres have given kind assistance in supplementing my own observations and directing me to sources of information, and besides those mentioned in the text or in connection with the photographs, I wish to express my profound thanks to the following:

Mrs. John D. Alden, the library of the American Museum of Natural History, Mrs. Fritz G. Anderson, Mrs. May Lamberton Becker and the *New York Herald Tribune,* Mrs. A. W. Bosworth, Mr. Charles Barrett of Melbourne, Australia, Mrs. W. H. Buist of Dundee, Scotland, Mr. Thomas B. Couser, Miss Edith Dudley of the International Silk Guild, Fairchild Sons, Doctor Walter Granger, The Genetics Institute of Cambridge, England, Mr. P. Lechmere Guppy of Port of Spain, Trinidad, Doctor Edward Greenly of Bangor, North Wales, Mrs. Agnes V. Hildebrand, Mrs. Anna L. Holladay, Doctor H. S. Jennings, Mrs. Harry U. Kibbe and the Bide-A-Wee Home Association for Friendless Animals, Mrs. G. Kirchmann, Mr. Robert J. Lanier, Mrs. James Mackie, Jr., Captain Thomas I. Miller, Mr. Chih Meng and the China Institute in America, New York Public Library, New England Rendering Company, Doctor Leon Roth, Doctor Jacob L. Reighard, G. Schirmer, Inc., Mr. Franklin S. Smith, Doctor Edward L. Sander and The Humane Society of New York, Miss Viola P. Sherrill, Doctor A. C. St Amand, Doctor Mary M. Thomson, Mrs. Gertrude E. Taylor, The Theobald Industries, Miss Phyllis M. Thomas and the Zoological Museum of Tring, England, Miss Eunice C. Wilson, Rudolph Wurlitzer Company, Doctor Donald Wyman and the Arnold Arboretum of Harvard University.

IDA M. MELLEN

Brooklyn, New York

Contents

Contents ix

Illustrations

PART ONE

THE CAT'S EVOLUTIONARY STATUS

Mission of the Cat Family
Distribution of the Domestic Cat
Unknown Origin
Variation Under Domestication

Chapter One

THE GREAT CAT FAMILY—ITS MISSION

ALL THE CATS in the world, from the domestic pussy to the Bengal tiger, fall into one great family—the Felidæ. The wide distribution of this family, totaling some fifty or sixty extant species (mammalogists disagree upon the number of subspecies), is illustrated by the fact that it has representatives in nearly every part of the globe except the Arctic regions, Australia, New Zealand, Polynesia, Madagascar, and southeastern Malaysia. North America lays claim to as many as five groups, divided into about nine species, with perhaps fifteen subspecies.

Our household species naturally represents the smallest and gentlest of this great family, and although the lion still is called "the king of beasts" and formerly was regarded by naturalists as the superior of the tiger, the tiger now ranks as the largest, fiercest and most powerful of cats.

Among the gradations between these smallest and largest of felines occur many interesting forms, including the well-known cheeta or hunting leopard of southern India, which can be led on a leash and long has been celebrated as a companion of royalty in Africa, Asia, and Europe. The cheeta's ability to run for short distances with great velocity has been enlisted for several thousand years in hunting the water buck. The jaguar, which ranges north into Texas, New Mexico and Arizona, readily is recognized as the largest and most bloodthirsty of American tigers. Another large cat is the puma or mountain lion, called the "mysterious puma" because of its shy and generally friendly attitude toward man. These two, with the lynx, jaguarundi and ocelot, make up the five North American groups. Our American bobcat or bay lynx holds a prominent place in the lynx tribe, as does also the Canadian lynx or "big gray wild cat," called "the patron of lovers" because of its occasional overtures toward couples strolling in the woods. Other species of lynxes include the caracal or Persian lynx, which is trained to hunt birds, and less familiar cats embrace the pampas cat of Patagonia, the colocolo and margay, also of South America, the rusty-spotted cat of Madras and Ceylon, the small-eared, long-haired cat of China and Mongolia, and others.

So important is the cat family among quadrupeds that it is placed at the head of the carnivores. Beautiful and muscular of body and limb, graceful, lithe and clothed in fur, its movements are quick and its feet digitigrade, while the spine in the smaller species is flexible and the skin loose. The rounded head (particularly round in the short-faced species such as the domestic cat and its wild congeners) can be turned in any direction, the claws are sharp and hooked, the tongue strong and rough, the teeth include prominent canines, and most species have arboreal habits, climbing trees for protection and to locate their prey.

Though the lion favors sandy plains, and the tiger and others prefer the jungle, some felines inhabit hills and rocky ledges, some, such as wild cats, live largely in trees, while others, which do more or less fishing, are found in the neighborhood of lakes and streams. Most of the Felidæ enjoy warmth, yet the puma withstands the severest winters of the Rocky Mountains, and the Canadian lynx and ounce or snow leopard of Central Asia also endure great cold, their fur being thick and long.

When man evolved scarcely more than a million years ago, the cat family was already old in time, certain species having existed over forty million years before his advent. Since some of the fifty extinct species which have been unearthed had attained a length of fourteen feet, it is remarkable that primitive man was able to maintain his species in the face of such formidable enemies, and there is no doubt that these large cats, ranging over almost the entire globe, had considerable to do with the very slow growth in his population. Though their most ancient remains thus far discovered are represented by fossils of the lower Oligocene period of the earth's history in Europe and North America, about thirty-eight million years ago, the Felidæ originated much earlier, since by that time they had evolved into two highly specialized groups now designated as true cats and saber-toothed tigers. Nowhere have these extinct species been discovered in larger numbers and more varied forms than in the United States, and the birthplace of the family may be here.

Alfred S. Romer believes that the saber-tooths, which preyed on the pachyderms, disappeared earlier from Europe because of the extinction of the mastodons at the beginning of the Ice Age, and that the increase in the numbers of the true cats was due to the increasing number of smaller types, such as horses and antelopes, which formed easy prey for them. Lions and tigers still lingered in Europe during the historic period, lynxes are said to persist today in some wild mountainous regions, and four varieties of *Felis sylvestris,* including three varieties of European wild cat and the British wild cat (*F. sylvestris grampia*), are extant though the British wild cat is said now to be confined to the Scottish Highlands, where its numbers greatly multiplied during the World War when persecutions ceased.

From what sort of animal the cats originated is unknown (their nearest living relative appears to be the fossa of Madagascar), but the heavy round head and tiny, forward-pointing ears of cubs and kittens, and other conspicuous differences between the kitten and the cat point to some immensely distant Eocene ancestor quite different from any cats we know; and we cannot even guess what was the mission on earth of that most remote ancestor nor why it became extinct. In the course of evolution the teeth and jaw muscles of the cat tribe have moved forward and the jaws have shortened, bringing their power to bear prominently on the canine teeth, and it is not difficult to determine the mission of the cats, great and small, in this flesh-eating world—by which we mean their part in maintaining "Nature's balance." If it is the mission of the spider to eat the fly, the wasp to kill the spider, the dragon fly and the bat to destroy the mosquito; of the beaver to check the growth of the forests; of the bird to keep down the number of insects and fruit trees and members of its own race; of the shark to prey on the sea turtle; of frogs, salamanders and fishes to destroy one another; and of the coyote to limit the population of prairie dogs, ground squirrels, rabbits and grouse, then the mission of the larger cats is to prey on wild sheep, goats, deer, dogs, large rodents, cattle and the monkey tribe, and of the smaller cats to check the multiplication of small rodents, snakes, and birds. The Canadian lynx eats ground hogs, squirrels, birds, raccoons, rabbits, rats, shrews and mice, and is an important forest scavenger. In parts of the United States the bobcat or bay lynx (*Felis lynx* or *Lynx rufus rufus*) is considered of great value in checking the spread of wood rats, mice and rabbits. If among the Felidæ the tiger, lion, leopard and panther have a mission peculiar to themselves, no doubt it is to limit the human population, and in Africa and Asia the big cats take a heavy toll of human lives.

Under association with man most animals forget their primary usefulness on earth, but it will be seen that the domestic cat still recognizes its part in maintaining "Nature's balance" when it hunts for snakes, birds and rodents. For this reason and because of the animal's determined refusal to be subjugated, it is commonly stated that the cat never has been completely tamed.

HOW MAN UPSETS NATURE'S BALANCE

In Western Australia domestic cats gone wild are doing great damage to marsupials and birds such as the honeymouse, night parrot, and other creatures small enough for them to prey upon. In most countries domestic cats gone wild have been driven from their homes by the cruelty of human beings and forced to get their food by returning to the feral state. In Western Australia the cats were compelled to run wild with the short-sighted object of having them reduce the number of rabbits which were destroying agriculture; and it was prohibited to wound, kill, capture, sell or dispose of any domestic cat run wild or at large "within the whole state of Western Australia without a special permit in that behalf." Fifteen years ago this interference with the order of nature, so typical of the human race in every "civilized" land, led to the discovery that as the little marsupials and birds ate insects which were injurious to the trees, the diminution of their numbers by the cats was bound to prove harmful to the growth of the forests.

Perhaps a sufficient commentary on this matter lies in the fact that Nature never planted a wild cat in Australia. We suspect, also, that the natural enemies of the rabbits had been exterminated by human agency.

Chapter Two

THE DISTRIBUTION OF THE DOMESTIC CAT

(*Its Unknown Origin and Variation Under Domestication*)

THE CAT is called "the first pet of civilization" and its domestication "one of the greatest triumphs of human perseverance," but the beginnings of its domestication are lost in antiquity—it may have been the pet of savages before civilizations existed—and in the light of present-day knowledge, taming the wild ancestors of our domestic cats may have required no great perseverance.

The fact that the cat still retains certain qualities and instincts of the wild is regarded by some scholars as indicating a domestication later than the dog's. On the other hand, the dog's sense of smell is believed to be keener, and this, it is held, indicates the cat's earlier taming, since smell is the first of the senses to deteriorate under domestication. The dog also remains a ready biter.

It has been suggested that the servile spirit of the dog and the independence of the cat are due to the fact that the dog normally lives and hunts in packs and therefore has a racial habit of obeying a leader, the weaker fawning on the stronger and the young bullying the old, while the cat normally lives and hunts singly or in pairs and each is its own master.

After more than forty-five hundred known years of association with man, cat breeds number considerably less than those of the dog, which varies enormously under domestication. All cat breeds that have ever evolved, *i.e.,* those that are extant and those that have come and gone, probably would not total much above thirty-five, with an indeterminate number of sub-breeds.* Cat breeds commonly are referred to as varieties, but no variety status can be conferred upon an animal without a knowledge of its origin, and as the origin of the domestic cat remains unknown, it is therefore, world over, of but one genus and species, without subspecies (varieties).

The name *Felis domestica,* in common use, was given by Gmelin in 1788; but the name *Felis catus* had been given by Linnæus in 1758, and biological ethics requires the recognition of the first name given. Elliot lists several variety names which were proposed but failed, as *F. catus,* var. *domesticus,* 1777; *F. catus,* var. *angorensis,* 1778; *F. catus,* var. *hispanicus,* 1788; *F. catus,* var. *cæruleus,* etc. Lydekker is said to have called the Siamese cat a distinct species, *F. siamensis,* and a recent children's encyclopedia gives variety names for the Angora and Manx, thus: *F. domesticus angorensis, F. domesticus ecaudatus.* These names are without scientific standing, and the domestic cat of all breeds remains *Felis catus.*

The word *cat,* coming down the ages from ancient oriental

---

*No one has ever traveled about the world studying cat breeds (an undertaking which would be well worth while), but breeds generally known today number five or six long-haired and about sixteen short-haired, with at least fifteen sub-breeds, three of which have recently become extinct. Twenty-seven breeds and sub-breeds are mentioned in this book.

sources, has fixed itself in nearly every tongue. Major Stanley S. Flower tells us that the Nubian word for cat is Kadîs, while the Egyptians call the male cat Kut and the female Kutta. In almost any country in the world the traveler would be understood if he referred to a cat as *cat.**

If the wild dog was tamed to aid man in the chase, it is reasonable to conclude that the wild cat was tamed to aid woman in the protection of the grain when first she hoarded this for winter use. This may have occurred ten thousand years ago. Some scholars believe that the cat was domesticated before granaries were thought of and that it became much better appreciated when it undertook the protection of the grain. Others believe that the marten was first tamed in both Africa and Europe and was superseded in the course of time by the more satisfactory cat, or that the cat and marten were tamed together in these countries when rats and mice began to infest human habitations.

For the earliest evidences of the domestication of the cat, Egyptologists point to 6th Dynasty graves, which contain cat figures. These date from 2600 B.C. The *Book of the Dead* mentions and figures the animal, and coffins of 2400 B.C. are inscribed with the seventeenth chapter of the *Ritual,* in which the cat appears. Its domestication, however, may have begun much earlier in Nubia, from whence it may have been introduced into Egypt.

The cat in the celebrated fowling scene depicted on a wall painting from an 18th Dynasty tomb now in the Egyptian collection of the British Museum is regarded by some Egyptologists not as a household pet, but as a hunting

*"Cat," by Ida M. Mellen, *The Cat Courier,* April, 1938.

cat used in a manner similar to that in which the cheeta is used. The cat is shown eagerly waiting for its master to toss the throwing stick as a signal for it to leap from the boat and fetch the quarry from the thicket. Since birds represented meat to the Egyptians and the natural prey of the wild cat consists of birds and rodents, it may not have been difficult to procure its services in retrieving the birds brought down. The cat which sits under the chair of a woman on a limestone tablet from the tomb of Meri-meri (18th or 19th Dynasty), now in the Rijksmuseum in Leiden, Netherlands, is undeniably a house cat. At this time, approximately 1500 to 1300 B.C., Egypt was at the height of her grandeur and the cat had been tame for many centuries. It is believed that the Egyptians kept several breeds of cats. Herdman, it is said, identified cat mummies taken to Liverpool as those of the Kaffir cat, *F. caffra,* a wild cat found commonly today all over Africa and having at least a dozen other specific names.

The Egyptians, as is well known, developed great skill in taming wild creatures such as the hawk, dog, ibis, crocodile and others; but all the animals they tamed save the dog and the common cat reverted to the wild state, and that the Kaffir cat numbers among the species that once were tamed admits of little dubiety. Tame hawks and cats accompanied the Egyptians to distant wars, but always were carried home, even if they had died, that they might be properly embalmed and interred in holy ground; and it is upon the Phœnicians that the responsibility is laid for the wide distribution of the domestic cat, which they got from the Egyptians and carried everywhere. The obviously composite ancestry of the cat of today is ascribed to the fact that cats in various countries where they were sold or left

The cat pictured on the tomb of Meri-meri existed when Egypt was at the height of her grandeur and cats had been tame for many centuries. Note the long, upstanding ears.

Tortoise-shell-and-white cat, Peter, a sterile male studied by Doctor Clyde E. Keeler at the Harvard Medical School to identify the animal in the literature. The colors are white, black and red.

by Phœnician traders interbred with the native wild cats and thus gave rise to breeds of new form and color and slightly different traits, though some breeds, such as tailless cats, kink-tailed cats and pendulous-eared cats apparently arose as biological "sports," that is, by mutation. Climatic conditions also have effected singular changes in cats, such as those described by the German naturalist, Johann Rudolph Rengger, a century ago (see Bibliography). The domestic cat, though introduced from Europe into Paraguay less than two hundred years previous to Rengger's day, had changed its habits, its colors, its coat, and in some cases even its size. It never became wholly wild, though it lived at the edges of the forests except during the rainy seasons, when it sought human habitations for protection, being too delicate to withstand rain and cold. The colors of a minority remained the same as those of the European house cat, but wild gray with black markings predominated, and in size some were "almost a quarter smaller" than the cats at Asuncion, where they mated with freshly introduced individuals and therefore remained truer to type. Altered males, however, were of the same size as the European house cat. The symmetry was perfect, the limbs dainty and very agile, but the hair had become "short, more glossy, thin, stranded and scantily interwoven, being shorter still on the tail"; and the animal looked frail.*

*Through a misstatement by Mivart, to the effect that this cat was but one-fourth the size of the ordinary domestic cat instead of but one-fourth smaller, as Rengger had stated, the Paraguayan cat, even today, is wrongly recorded in our encyclopedias as a "dwarf cat" weighing only three pounds when adult. Lydekker suggested that the cat seemed to have some affinity with the jaguarundi, and so the encyclopedias state that the jaguarundi may have been its ancestor—which is not possible. See "The Origin of the Mexican Hairless Cat," by Ida M. Mellen, *Journal of Heredity,* October, 1939.

This cat appears to have been intermediate between the common domestic cat and the New Mexican (called also Mexican) hairless cat, which formerly was exhibited at cat shows in the United States and which undoubtedly sprang from the Paraguayan cat. This hairless cat was most often mouse colored with pink belly, though it revealed faint stripes and other evidences of tabby ancestry. In winter it developed a ridge of fur along the back and upper surface of the tail. Both these interesting cats, whose numbers never greatly increased, appear to be extinct, and if so, they illustrate the impermanence of mutants when these arise as late adaptations of animals standardized by long association with man. Moreover, it has been established by a French veterinary professor, Etienne Letard, that hairlessness is a recessive trait, his observations having been made upon the occurrence of hairless kittens from the mating of a certain pair of normal Siamese cats.* Another mutant of this kind appeared in the United States, in the litter of a North Carolina domestic feline, the animal having obtained wide publicity as a doglike cat. Later it gave birth to normal kittens.† The Australian cat, no longer seen, was a mutant from normal Siamese cats and had extremely short hair, with short whiskers or none.

In the Kaffir cat the face and general proportions correspond with those of our domestic species, though the muscles are more powerful. The coat is short and frequently the color is tawny gray with light black stripes on body and legs somewhat like those of the domestic striped tabby or

*Journal of Heredity, May, 1938.
†Journal of Heredity, March and September, 1937, articles by Henry Sternberger.

tiger cat, a yellow or nearly white belly, and a long, rather thick ringed tail with a black tip. The cat shows the beginnings of the letter M in its forehead, has long, upstanding ears, two transverse streaks on the cheeks (these cheek lines are common to almost all wild cats), and rings around the neck. The soles of the hind feet are dark and the legs long. It resembles the domestic cat of Egypt pictured in the murals and other paintings of the days of the Pharaohs. Some specimens, however, show intermediate stages leading to the present domestic type of Abyssinian ticked cat, and according to Brooke (see Bibliography) the Egyptian cat of a thousand years later than the Pharaohs is represented with the brown body, yellow belly and barred legs and tail of the brown Abyssinian. The cat's early record in the land of Cush (Ethiopia) harmonizes with the belief that the present-day ticked cat of Abyssinia is of a very ancient type, not unlike some of the cats of the late dynasties of Egypt. Early Indian domestic cats are recorded as having been of two types, spotted and red with barred legs, and these, it is believed, also traced their ancestry through devious stages back to the Kaffir cat, with a plentiful admixture of Indian wild cats.

To the Kaffir cat it still is believed that our pet cats of today may almost certainly look as one of their first tamed ancestors, though they have also the blood of many another wild cat, including, without doubt, Temminck's golden cat (*F. temmincki*) of Borneo, Burma, etc., the forehead of which is plainly marked with a jew's-harp, so often seen also in our modern domestic cats.

In ancient geologic times a land connection existing between Spain and Africa permitted the Kaffir cat to roam over northeastern Africa and a considerable part of Europe, and its remains have been found fossil in Belgium and the cavern deposits of the Rock of Gibraltar, also in the British Isles, which were connected with the mainland of Europe in ancient times, together with those of animals long extinct.

Historians have pointed out that to the Assyrians, Babylonians and Hebrews the cat evidently was unknown as a domestic animal. Assyrian monuments depict the cheeta hunting, but Assyrians and Babylonians both included lions and panthers among dogs, which it is thought they hardly could have done had they been familiar with the house cat. The failure of Hebrew writers of antiquity to mention the Egyptian cat is attributed to the fact that while serving in bondage they learned to hate everything that was sacred to the Egyptians. Nor is the cat mentioned in the Bible except in a single reference, probably to a wild cat, in the Apocrypha, Baruch vi., 22, where the gods of the Babylonians are described as of wood and silver and gold, fashioned by carpenters and goldsmiths, and "Upon their bodies and heads sit bats, swallows, and birds, and the cats also."

Mention of the cat in Sanscrit writings of three thousand years ago makes it seem probable that the domestication of this animal in Egypt or Nubia may have been coincident with if not actually subsequent to its domestication in India. It received but scant attention from Greek and Roman writers of antiquity, and to the dog-loving Greeks is ascribed the eclipse of cat worship which followed their destruction of Egyptian culture.

Some scholars think that in European countries bordering the Mediterranean the cat was tamed during the Bronze Age, a rather indefinite term, but the dates may be about

2000 to 1800 B.C.; and the Lake Dwellers of Switzerland are believed to have kept tame cats and to have eaten wild ones (about 2000 B.C.).

In China the domestication of the cat at a very early date has led to the conjecture that tame short-haired specimens reached that country from India, another supposition being that native wild cats were locally tamed. Both theories may be correct.

The biographies of some of the great founders of oriental religions and philosophies mention the cat. Confucius, about 500 B.C., watched his cat catching a mouse. Muhammad, about 600 A.D., often lifted his cat to finish the milk in his bowl or stood in the pulpit preaching to his disciples with the animal in his arms. This cat may have come from Syria, where an early domesticated breed existed. Muhammad's disciples do not mention her name.

In Japan the domestic cat, known many centuries ago, is said to have been introduced from China by way of Korea and Manchuria; and Takakuwa shows that it was appreciated not only by the people but at the Imperial Court, as indicated by a reference to the animal in the Emperor Uda's diary of 890.

Although the Crusaders did not introduce the modern domestic cat into Europe or the British Isles, as has sometimes been stated, they carried back with them the cheeta and probably the civet. The domestic cat was certainly there hundreds of years before the first of the Crusades (1096) and, indeed, long before the Christian era began in the middle of the eighth century. Several centuries before Christ the Romans and Greeks undoubtedly imported a few cats now and then from the banks of the Nile. Cats, nevertheless, still were so rare in Europe and the British Isles, and so valuable in the time of Henry the Fowler (876–936), that his Code prescribed a fine of sixty bushels of corn for the wilful murder of an adult mouser, and at about the same time the laws of Switzerland, Saxony and Wales imposed heavy fines on cat killers. It is well known that as late as the beginning of the fifteenth century, in Dick Whittington's time, a cat was worth its weight in gold in some parts of the world.

In the absence of definite knowledge concerning the introduction of the tame cat into the British Isles, it is surmised that the animal arrived there with the Romans. According to Lydekker the remains of cats apparently of the domestic breed have been discovered in England in Roman villas. Mivart felt certain that when Julius Cæsar invaded England in 55–54 B.C. there was not a single mouser in any British town or village, though the forests were plentifully supplied with wild cats. Since the Roman evacuation took place early in the fifth century, more than three hundred years before the beginning of the Christian era, one contention is that our modern western cats resulted from a cross between the ancient Roman pussy and the British wild cat. This British wild cat, called "the British tiger," though longer haired and larger than the Kaffir cat, reveals somewhat similar colors, yellowish gray with dark brown wavy stripes on body and legs (these stripes being broader and more numerous than the Kaffir cat's), the "locket" that has proved so difficult to eradicate in domestic cats of solid color, and a ringed bushy tail, truncated and tipped with black. It is larger also than the domestic cat, but like the Kaffir cat resembles the striped tabby, and the letter M may be seen in the forehead more plainly than in any other wild cat. Another theory, based on the fact that the Dutch are said to have called their tabby cats Cyprian cats, is that tabbies and tortoise-shells reached England from the island of Cyprus with merchants seeking tin.

The tamed Egyptian cat had only to be transported across the Strait of Gibraltar to reach Spain and Portugal, and in the latter country it has some distinctive descendants today. Major Stanley S. Flower kindly sends us the following note from his unpublished observations of cats in Portugal (1935):

Lisbon might be described as a city of cats. Most of them are smaller than English domestic cats, with longer, very upstanding ears and long legs. Some individuals that I examined carefully were practically identical in eyes, size, proportions and markings with the true *Felis libyca* [*F. caffra*] of Egypt, but in the domestic cat of Portugal irregular patches of white often spoil the harmonious colour of the wild African cat.

If all breeds of *F. catus* could be narrowed down to their beginnings, there is some reason to believe that gray lined and striped tabbies or tiger cats would figure most prominently in the ancestral stock, followed by the finely spotted cat in which the stripes have begun to disintegrate, and the ticked cat in which the disintegration is more pronounced. Tortoise-shell cats and those of solid color came later. The origin of the blotched tabby, however, is quite unknown, but it is supposed to have arisen west of the Orient as a direct mutation of the striped tabby or from some extinct wild cat. There appears to be only one wild cat with decidedly blotched sides, the "little marbled tiger" of Asia (*F. marmorata*), pictured and described by Elliot as of larger size than the domestic cat, with a much longer tail and short, upstanding ears.

Some hybrids of the British domestic cat and British wild cat are said to resemble the Abyssinian ticked cat, and ordinary striped tabbies sometimes produce kittens ticked very much like it, some with a ground color of gray or blue, exhibiting a reversion to the ancient type. The fur of the Abyssinian cat differs from a rabbit's only in that the under coat is rufous, the upper grayish coat being ticked with dark brown like a Belgian hare's, *i.e.*, each hair is dark tipped, which produces the ticking. The black-tipped tail, necklaces, cheek stripes and "M" in the forehead, particularly in the kitten, reveal the wild African ancestry. Seafaring men brought home to New England several breeds of cats from Europe and the Orient, tailed and tailless, long-haired and short-haired, and in this country we have today strange mixtures of these breeds.

Not the least perplexing problem presented by this great family of carnivores is the evolution of the colors of felines of all species. Solid colors, now much sought after by professional breeders of domestic cats, result from generations of artificial selection and can be held only by meticulous care in maintaining the purity of the breeding stock; for only after three, or sometimes five selected generations in crossbreeding does success begin to attend the breeder's efforts, and fifteen or more generations later throwbacks may still occur to the colors of the original stock. Natural selection seldom has produced a species of feline or even an individual of uniform color. White is rare among them, albinism rarer.*

*A nearly white tiger and a nearly white cheeta are exhibited in the British Museum, but Mr. R. I. Pocock informs us that no record exists of their original eye color. He is certain they were not albinos. An albino leopard from East Africa is among the mounted felines in the Zoological Museum of Tring. (Lord Rothschild said it had pink eyes.)

Black felines are not common, though every zoological park and circus now displays a black leopard, black jaguars and tigers have been recorded, and it is said that a black wild cat once was shown at the Jardin des Plantes. Some naturalists hold that black felines originally existed in a state of nature as distinct breeds. If so, they were fatally conspicuous in the midst of a green world and lost in the race for survival. Few of the large cats are unspotted, and commonly when a species is clearly of one color in the adult stage, as in the lion, the cubs reveal distinct spots, indicating a spotted ancestor. Though the larger cats do not normally interbreed, the domestic cat always is willing to mate with a wild cat, though the period of their gestation differs. Major Stanley S. Flower informs us that in Egypt today domestic cats may be seen which are tortoise-shell, fawn-and-white, and yellow (marmalade), colors which must have been produced in late centuries by promiscuous breeding. Chance variations of white and black, commingled with the original wild cat colors of red and gray (some with black-tipped tails and whitish breasts) may have brought about the variety in fixed colors and color-patterns which have been perpetuated by artificial selection. The incidence of white in the domestic cat is of special significance. We are informed by Mr. T. H. Gillespie, Director of the Zoological Park in Edinburgh, Scotland, that in some hybrids of a male wild cat and female domestic cat marked with tortoise-shell-and-white, the white was conspicuous, and when these hybrids cross-bred the resulting litter was entirely white except for brindled patches, illustrating the strong natural dominance of white over other colors.

The origin of the long-haired cat also is obscure. The British wild cat strongly resembles the long-haired breeds, which it is believed evolved entirely from long-haired wild cats and not as mutations of short-haired breeds; and it is important in this connection to note that the colors of long domesticated long-haired and short-haired cats are almost identical. Long-haired cats occur as separate breeds in various eastern countries including China, Angora, Burma,* Afghanistan, Persia, and Russia, and it is commonly held that Pallas' Tibetan cat (*F. manul*) of the deserts of Central Asia is the ancestor of the Persian breed. Mr. R. I. Pocock considers, however, that there is no evidence that English domestic long-haired cats originated in Persia or Asia Minor, and believes that a long-haired breed may have been fostered in ancient times in countries lying near the eastern end of the Mediterranean. In Pallas' cat, which is slightly smaller than the Egyptian cat, the long, soft fur is light gray, with stripes on the body and rings on the rather short, black-tipped, bushy tail; and the animal exhibits the two horizontal cheek lines characteristic of most wild and domesticated cats, the beginnings of the letter M in the forehead, and a whitish chin and throat.

Pallas himself stated that long-haired cats were taken from China to Siberia, and it is evident that the Phœnicians have had many imitators in the custom of transporting cats to strange lands. Cats also distribute themselves to some extent, many reports having been received of the sudden appearance of a cat at some home isolated by miles from all other human habitations.

In 1891 John Lockwood Kipling wrote that Persian cats, which were greatly prized in India as family pets, were

---

*The long-haired Burmese cat has Siamese coloring and white feet, while the short-haired Burmese is walnut brown.

"brought down from Kabul [the capital of Afghanistan] by the Provendahs, a tribe of Afghan dealers who brought camel caravans with various kinds of produce into the Punjab every winter"; and in 1928 Takakuwa wrote that long-haired cats still were being imported into India from Afghanistan after being tamed at Kabul. Though they are called Persian cats, Persia has not a sufficient number of cats for exportation. Apparently they yield easily to domestication, and it is certain that other species of wild cats also are readily tamed. Mr. T. H. Gillespie informs us that in his opinion, "any wild kitten of *any* species, if taken young enough, can be made very tame." He exhibited in his zoo in Edinburgh at one time a very tame serval (African wild cat, *Felis serval*), and says (1939), "We had a Scottish wild kitten not long ago which had been taken from the nest and reared by hand and was extremely tame—undoubtedly a genuine wild cat."

ARTIFICIAL SELECTION

In both eastern and western hemispheres astonishing changes in color of coat and eyes and other physical characters of the domestic breeds, long-haired and short-haired, have been effected by cat fanciers. Natural characteristics considered undesirable, such as cross-eyes and kinked tails in the Siamese, hazel eyes in the silver tabby, gray ground color and green eyes in the blotched tabby, dark gray coat and yellow or hazel eyes in the chinchilla cat, green eyes in white, black, and other cats, white breasts and tabby markings in cats of solid color, etc., have been eliminated; and new breeds have been fixed by the improvement of sports, or deliberately produced by genetic experimentation. One breed of cat may become completely submerged in another, as in the case of the Angora cat which, in cross-breeding with the Persian, is dominated by the latter, whose characteristics are better liked; and one new type of cat called the Peke-face is required to resemble a Pekinese dog in its physiognomy. There is no end to the wonders that may be performed by persistent and intelligent artificial selection.

From the biological point of view too great credit cannot be given to cat breeders, largely people without scientific training, for the remarkable results they have achieved. They have been obliged to learn which traits and which colors are dominant and which recessive; exactly how to outbreed an unwanted trait; that throwbacks to the original stock may occur after many generations of selective breeding and specimens not up to type must be consigned to the chloroform box. The difficulties under which they have labored are illustrated by such facts as these:

The tailless Manx cat after four or five decades of careful breeding still produces some tailed offspring.

Tortoise-shell, tortoise-shell-and-white, and blue cream males are scarce and apt to be sterile (the reason for which is not understood).

Females are rare among yellow cats.

Lined tabby dominates over striped tabby and both over brown tabby; black dominates over smoke and blue; brown tabby dominates over blue, black, smoke and red. White cats with blue or yellow eyes may dominate all other colors.

ALBINO CATS

Albinism, though not known among the smaller Felidæ in a state of nature, doubtless has occurred. In the domestic felines it so seldom is seen that among several hundred

Pirate of Glen Orry, cream male Manx kitten, seven months old, bred by the Misses Ruth and Ellen Carlson.

Mexican hairless cats, a breed apparently extinct.

INEXPLICABLE BREEDS

No tailless or hairless felines occur in nature, yet both conditions arise
in the domestic species, the former being common over
a wide Asiatic area and in the Isle of Man, the
latter occurring as a mutant in various breeds.

PRODUCTS OF ARTIFICIAL SELECTION

Top: Short-haired silver tabby. Note jew's-harp in forehead. Champion Prince Charming of the Mosque was owned by Doctor Frances L. MacCraken of Detroit. *Bottom:* Chinchilla Persian Champion Bonnie Maid o' the Mist, owned by Miss Maud Lantry of New York.

people, cat judges, cat breeders, veterinarians, and others, interviewed or corresponded with by the author, only two had ever seen an albino cat. It is said that they formerly were not uncommon in England, but no standing was allotted to them at cat shows and therefore no effort was made to fix the strain. An albino cat or family of albinos comes to light in the United States about once in twenty-five years, one of the most remarkable cases having been strangely overlooked by the naturalist, Richard Lydekker. In his *A Hand Book of the Carnivora,* 1895, he described a new breed of thick-furred cat which he said had been produced in the cold storage warehouses of Pittsburgh, but apparently the story was taken from a newspaper, for he failed to learn that the cats were albinos.

This is his report: Rats adapted themselves to the below freezing temperatures of the warehouses and appeared clothed, body and tail, in wonderful thick fur. After many unsuccessful attempts to adapt the domestic feline enemies of the rat to the extreme cold, one of the warehouse companies succeeded when a female cat produced seven kittens which, by great care, were reared and distributed among other warehouses. Thus a special breed of cat was established with thick under-fur like Canadian lynxes, short tails, chubby bodies, and very long whiskers to guide them in the dim light in hunting their prey; but they died in a few hours if exposed to the open air in summer.

This story has been repeated, with more or less elaboration, by the writers of many cat books, not the least diverting version being that of a Dutch naturalist, who solemnly avers that the object in placing the cats in the "ice box" was to breed them for their fur and that it did produce a most luxuriant coat; but they finally became such thick round balls of fur that it was impossible for them to move about!

The facts, as nearly as can be ascertained after the lapse of years, and with only one person living who remembers this cat family, are substantially as follows: An employé of a Pittsburgh cold storage warehouse owned a pair of cats. The female gave birth to kittens in a room known as the freezer, where the temperature ranges from zero to five degrees above zero. These kittens were not distributed among other warehouses, for there were no others in the city at that time. There had been no attempt to establish a special breed of cat to combat the rat, because there were not then and never have been any rats in the warehouse; and this family of cats became extinct. The kittens could not endure the warm outdoor air, nor could they tolerate a bright light; their fur was thick, otherwise they differed in no way from ordinary cats except for their eyes, which were pink. The hearing of the kittens was good. Both parents were white, and the mother is known to have had pink eyes. This is one of the rare authenticated cases of albino cats occurring in the United States. Cats follow the laws of heredity governing recessive traits, among which albinism is included. The father of the warehouse kittens, therefore, was either an albino like the mother, or came of albinic stock, for an entire family of albino kittens can be produced only by such parental combinations as these. If one parent is an albino and the other normal and not of albinic stock, all the kittens will be pigmented. If both parents are pigmented but come of albinic stock, only one in four of the kittens will be an albino.

These cats would have afforded priceless material for the study of albinism, and possibly in cross-breeding experiments might have thrown some indirect light on the age-old problem of deafness in blue-eyed white cats; but the singular fact of their complete albinism was not discovered by Richard Lydekker or any other scientist of his day.

TORTOISE-SHELL CATS

Darwin believed that as tortoise-shell cats are almost always females and yellow cats are commonly males, the two must constitute natural pairs; but in the light of Mendelianism this has turned out not to be the case. Natural pairs would produce only kittens like themselves, and this does not happen. Black often predominates in such a cross, with red, tortoise-shell, and possibly cream (light yellow) in lesser numbers. In some instances not a single tortoise-shell kitten appears in the litter. Seldom in nature is there a color difference in the sexes among the Felidæ, though in certain wild cats living near the desert the wandering male is said to be lighter than the female, who remains near rocks and vegetation to protect her young; and Elliot's color plate of the pampas cat (*F. pajeros*) shows a color difference in the sexes. Mr. Pocock mentions that the only species of animals known to him to be tortoise-shell in a state of nature are the African hunting dog and the lemming.

Differently patterned tortoise-shell cats have arisen in different countries, due no doubt to the dissimilarities in the colors of local wild cats with which the domestic feline has interbred, and new sub-breeds, such as blue tortoise-shells in which blue replaces the black color, have been produced by artificial selection. It is said that since 1900 only twenty male tortoise-shell cats have appeared in England and that there are only five in that country at the present time, but two of which are fertile. A Danish cat fancier offered 10,000 kronen (about $2500) for one a few years ago, but failed to procure it. Doctor Joseph C. Thompson of San Francisco owns a male tortoise-shell, but whether other specimens exist in the United States is not known. Long-haired specimens are still rarer than short-haired. This breed has no present value in the western hemisphere except for cross-breeding experiments, but formerly male tortoise-shells brought prodigious prices in the Orient as "luck-bringers."

The approved pattern consists of rich and even patches of red, black and cream, with no tabby markings, no blurring or brindling of the colors, not one white hair, a blaze on the nose half black and half orange, and orange or copper eyes. Tortoise-shell-and-white cats are also called tortoise-shells, world over, and in these also the male is apt to be sterile. In the occasional fertile male, Doctor Clyde E. Keeler, geneticist of the Harvard Medical School, tells us that the spermatozoa carry the usual Y and X chromosomes, producing both male and female kittens.

The interesting question has been raised as to whether male tortoise-shell cats are not incomplete females. Ruth C. Bamber advances an alternative hypothesis that they may be males turned slightly toward the female condition—enough in many cases to make them sterile but not enough to mask their essential maleness; or they may be females turned almost entirely to the male condition—in either case "not very male males." She says, "Animals are not quite so sharply separated into male and female as has been commonly believed, but there are degrees of maleness and femaleness."

Doctor Clyde E. Keeler, one of the few who have worked out the Mendelian law for cats—which does not always correspond with the Mendelian law for some other animals, fishes, for example—regards the tortoise-shell cat as a genetically distinct breed, and says that in this cat the gene for red and the gene for black happen to lie in the sex chromosome, and when this fact is taken into consideration the results of the breeding of tortoise-shells are predictable.

THE MANX CAT

How and when the tailless cat reached the Isle of Man is not known. Some British authorities say it was first seen in Cornwall and called the Cornwall cat, others think it arrived in the Isle of Man in 1588 on one of the ships of the Spanish Armada which was wrecked on a rugged promontory of the island now known as Spanish Head, the cat having been carried by the Spaniards as a mascot. Still others think it arose as a sport of the common cat.

In Manx cats complete taillessness is a dominant trait, and only a cat lacking even the rudiments of a tail and having a depression or "dimple" at the end of the spine where the caudal vertebræ normally begin can be sold as a genuine Manx cat. The hind legs are longer than those of the domestic cat, and the gait is bobbing and stilted, but the animal does not hop. It balances perfectly, stands well on its hind legs, and in running leaps like a rabbit. Those who know the cat best say that it attains terrific speed. How long it can run in a straight line at this speed is not known, but the Misses Ruth and Ellen Carlson of

Glen Ellyn, Illinois, breeders of Manx cats, tell us that on a leash one of the males will trot and run three or four blocks at a stretch with accelerating speed, and in play two Manx kittens will chase each other with great rapidity for half an hour without stopping, back and forth over an open lawn 135 by 52 feet.

The head of the Manx cat is large and round and the coat double, the upper coat being soft and open and the under coat soft and thick. The colors are varied as in the domestic cat, with the usual striped and blotched tabby patterns, solid colors, and various mixtures of color. The Manx cat is a famous ratter, shy toward strangers but docile and devoted to its owner, courageous, and delights in driving strange dogs off the premises.

The American domestic bobtail cat of the New England and Middle Atlantic states (called also rabbit cat) traces its ancestry to the Manx cat, but the distribution of tailless and stump-tailed cats is wide, covering the Crimea and other parts of Russia, Japan, China, the Bismarck Archipelago, the Malayan Archipelago, Burma and Siam, their range overlapping that of the kink-tailed cat.

THE ANCIENT TABBIES

The lined and striped tabbies, called tigers, have been bred in Europe for four hundred years, and the blotched tabby, called tabby, was noticed by Linnæus in Sweden in 1746. In the tigers the ground color is gray, the sides marked with narrow (lined) or wide (striped) vertical bands running from the shoulder to the tip of the tail, and a black stripe runs down the back from head to tip of tail. The stripes, except for two transverse ones on each cheek, break up into spots about the face. The legs are barred with "bracelets," the chest ringed with "necklaces," the letter M marks the forehead, and the eyes generally are green.

In the brown or blotched tabby, which is a hardy breed like the tiger, the ground color originally was also gray and the eyes green, but after many years of selective breeding, choice specimens now show a ground color of seal brown, with orange eyes. The body color in this breed is offset with broad black stripes and swirls, or blotches, which present an appearance like moire silk, and the name of tabby is believed to derive from Atab, a street in Bagdad where moire or atabi silk is woven (though some scholars, perhaps in deference to the theory that this breed arose west of the Orient, trace it to "Sir Tybert the Catte" in the old German folk tale of Reynard the Fox). Three black stripes run down the back, with intervening brown stripes, two in number. The legs are evenly barred with high "bracelets" that meet the body markings. The tail is also barred, and the swirls on the sides form unbroken rings. "Necklaces" appear in distinct chainlike formation, and the facial markings between the ears and down the neck meet a "butterfly" on each shoulder. The letter M on the forehead and the two transverse cheek lines characteristic of many wild cats are present in this tabby as in the striped tabby.

Silver and blue blotched tabbies have been produced by artificial selection, these colors replacing the original gray or brown ground color and the markings being black; but in the red tabby, another sub-breed, the markings are only of a deeper orange than the body color.

Although a survey of our back-yard pussies appears to reveal some that are a mixture of tiger and tabby, experimental breeders say that a cross between the lined or striped tabbies or either of these with the brown tabby results in kittens resembling one or the other parent, with no admixtures, and these three are considered distinct breeds.

THE SIAMESE CAT

Since 1929 the popularity of the Siamese breed in the United States has increased enormously, although it made its first appearance in this country as early as 1895. It arrived in England in 1884, and we learn that like Manx and Persian cats, such large numbers have been exported from their home land that they now are more numerous in other countries. Though poetically called the "royal, sacred Siamese," this is the common cat of Siam and not restricted to palaces and temples.

The occasional large number of kittens occurring in this breed, the tenderness of the father, the persistence of the recessive coloring, the utter dependence of the cat on human companionship, all indicate that the Siamese has been kept as a pet for an incalculably long period of time.

The white fur of the kitten at birth, the fawn-colored body of the adult (marked with brown ears, muzzle, tail and feet), and its blue eyes, serve to classify it as a partial albino. Its colors are strongly suggestive of those of the Himalayan rabbit, which also is a member of the albino series. Iljin and Iljin's experiments convinced them that external temperatures affect the coat colors of the Siamese cat, particularly the male, and that the lower the temperature the darker will be the coat; and in the tropics, Mrs. Beatrice Greig of St. Augustine, Trinidad, informs us that the body of her eight-year-old male, Bahnu, has only slightly

Top: Young Siamese male cat, Cavalier of Newton. *Bottom:* Persian-Siamese male kitten, Per Thai, a triumph in modern genetics. Both bred and owned by Mrs. Virginia R. Cobb.

Top: Siamese mothers may produce large families. Nine of these kittens were in one litter. Bred, owned and photographed by Mrs. Virginia R. Cobb. *Bottom:* Most cats like potatoes and this one, Oliver, prefers them raw. Courtesy Mrs. Joseph Watson.

darkened, though his face has become darker. The Himalayan colors are similarly affected by temperature.

Natural characteristics of the Siamese cat, largely outbred in this country, are cross-eyes and kinked tails, but, though kink-tailed cats are common in Burma, the Malay Peninsula, Madagascar and the Philippine Islands, as well as in Siam, in no other known breed do cross-eyes normally occur, though they occur sporadically in the common cat.

LONG-HAIRED SIAMESE

Long-haired Siamese kittens have been produced by applied genetics, first in Sweden (about 1924) by Doctor K. Tjebbes, who used a white Persian in the cross and discovered that long hair and Siamese color are recessive traits, and secondly in the United States by Mrs. Virginia R. Cobb of Newton, Massachusetts.

After five years of experimentation based on the Mendelian law as prescribed by Doctor Clyde E. Keeler, Mrs. Cobb concluded (in 1935) the first successful American experiment in breeding long-haired Siamese kittens. She crossed with black Persian instead of white as in the Tjebbes experiments, using pedigreed sires and queens. The recessive traits of long hair and Siamese color have been combined in the kittens, which exhibit the blue eyes and in some cases the loquacity of the Siamese breed. The experiment, still in progress, may in time establish a distinct breed of cat representing a definite triumph in modern genetics. (See Bibliography.)

ANGORAS AND PERSIANS

The Angora appears to have been the first long-haired

cat introduced into the United States, its name deriving from Angora, now the capital of Turkey and famed for its long-haired dogs, goats, and cats. A great favorite with Turks and Armenians, the Angora breed is characterized by a pointed head, fairly long nose, ears of medium size, and eyes that sometimes are round and sometimes betray a slight slant. The fur is long and silky and the "Queen Elizabeth ruff" long and wavy, while the tail, which curls slightly upward toward the end, is bushy, with its longest hairs at the base.

In the Persian breed, whose original habitat, as previously explained, is not definitely known, the face is round, the nose short and broad (called "snub"), the ears short and the eyes large and round. The ruff is large, while the long fur is coarser than that of the Angora, and the animal stands lower on its legs. In its tail, which is carried straight or slightly downward, the longest hairs are found at the tip.

In the United States the Persian breed has submerged the Angora to such an extent that cat fanciers now refer to the product as "long-haired cats," and only those having the Persian characters are given a standing in the shows. In some continental countries, however, efforts still are made to keep the two breeds separate.

Chapter Three

WILD TRAITS IN THE
DOMESTIC CAT

GREAT CATS and small, though agreeing closely in general structure, differ in the structure of the brain, the shape of the pupil, and general behavior; and the fact that the domestic cat combines in a striking manner many traits and habits of some of the larger cats testifies to an ancient common ancestry. It retracts its claws like all the larger cats, purrs like the ocelot, the cheeta, the puma and others, and uses a scratching post like the tiger, leopard, and others. It climbs trees, as do most of the larger cats except the lion, tiger, and cheeta (and cheetas have been observed to leap into the low crotches of trees). Angora and Persian cats have ear tufts like some of the lynxes. Some breeds, such as the Manx and Siamese, have higher hind quarters like the ocelot and jaguarundi.* Like the bay lynx, the domestic cat has a beautiful face. In China there is a saying that the cat has the face of a tiger and the body of a *li,* the *li* being an exceedingly beautiful Chinese wild cat.

*For our information concerning the habits of the jaguarundi we are indebted to Mr. Harlan W. Major of New York City, who kindly permitted us to observe his jaguarundi, Negrito, which was taken when young and became sufficiently tame to be allowed the run of the house, though it was a one-man animal that only its master might touch.

Cats retrieve, play hide-and-seek, and box without instruction. The jaguarundi retrieves without instruction, and Miss Merlys Blakeslee of New York City informs us that her tame ocelot, Saba, would play hide-and-seek and box. Pumas, according to Hamilton Fyfe (*The Mystery of the Puma*), have been observed amusing themselves by the hour at hide-and-seek, and a pair of tigers in a zoo will box with each other. Many of the large cats jump on the back of an enemy and ride it out of the vicinity. In the same manner the domestic cat will leap on the back of an offending dog and ride it off the premises. As among the larger cats, males generally are not to be trusted with the young. Mother cats, like lionesses, pool their families, and when one wishes to absent herself the other remains on guard. Cats like to lie and sleep in the crotches of a tree like many of the wild cats. In stalking they creep along the ground like the lion and some other large cats. Like the puma they will follow people out of sheer curiosity. They seek notice and return caresses, and the clouded tiger of Sumatra, when tamed, is said to do the same. They are noisy at night like the jaguar. The domestic cat mews like the lynx and jaguarundi, calls for its mate as does the lynx, and as among lynxes the males caterwaul and quarrel when they meet. They play with their prey in the same manner in which a tiger has been observed to play with a human being it had captured.

Most members of the cat tribe are fond of birds, and several hundred years ago the Germans are said to have called the domestic cat a "tree rider," because it "hunteth birds and fowles from tree to tree." (Topsell, 1658.) It also eats bugs and grubs like the Canadian lynx. It is fond of catnip like the lynxes and wild cats, and loves perfumes

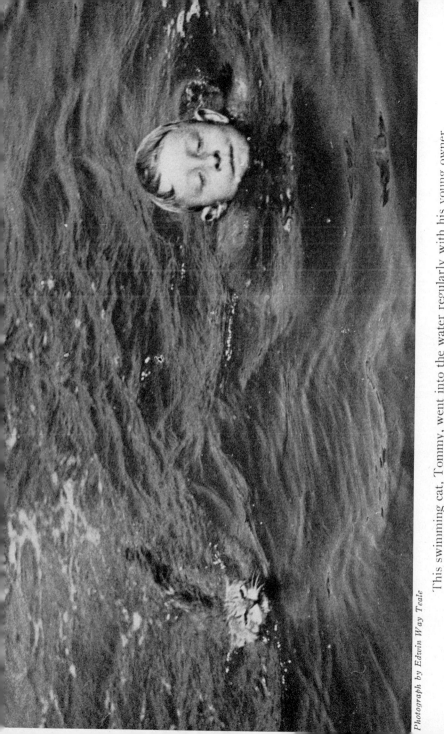

Photograph by Edwin Way Teale

This swimming cat, Tommy, went into the water regularly with his young owner, Master Mervin Bedell of Oceanside, New York.

This polydactyl cat, Duke, has twenty-four toes, six on each foot. He is owned by Mr. and Mrs. Valburg Kimball of Hamilton, N. Y.

like the panther, a specimen of which was tamed with lavender water. Some cats love lavender as much as catnip, and one that was accustomed to it refused to remain in her new home until her basket was sprayed with lavender. It has a taste for nuts, vegetables, and fruits like the jaguarundi, which is partial to bananas, coconut, and papaya. It is fond of white potatoes, and the lynx has exhibited a similar fondness. It is nervous like the jaguarundi and the ocelot. Like the jaguar it feels the day previously a coming change in the weather.

The shape of the pupil is believed by most mammalogists to govern the habits to a large extent. The lion, cheeta, fishing cat, and other felines with round pupils appear to be mainly diurnal, whereas species of cats with pupils that become vertically linear when contracted are able to see in a faint light in which their prey see but dimly, and it is believed that in consequence of this they have developed nocturnal habits. The domestic cat is one of these and its eyes gleam in semi-darkness like those of the panther and others. It has the same extraordinary powers of observation attributed to the lynx in the phrase "a lynx-eyed survey."

The habits of life of the wild species do not call for speed in pursuing their prey, and the ability of many to ascend trees affords better security from foes than fleetness of foot. Except for the cheeta, therefore, cats in general are held to be poor runners, but we have already described the habits of the Manx cat, which, like the cheeta, runs with remarkable speed. As the cheeta can attain great velocity only for short spurts, the Manx cat may be the swiftest of felines.

Traits crop out occasionally in individual cats similar to those of wild species. Many individuals among domestic felines love water and can swim as well as the jaguar or the tiger, or the lynxes which are said to be able to make two miles at a spurt; they go fishing like the jaguar, the lynxes, and the fishing cats of the Orient; they love to play with dripping water or with water in a receptacle, and some like to be out in the rain. It is said that domestic cats in certain parts of India test the temperature of the water with their paws and then jump in to fish. A swimming cat keeps its head, back, and tail above the water, while its ears are held in a horizontal position, folded slightly back to keep the interior dry. Tommy, a cat owned by Master Mervin Bedell of Oceanside, New York, regularly went swimming with his eight-year-old master. A cat owned by the author was happiest when provided with a large basin of water, which she splashed out with her fore paws until the basin was empty, and she could be summoned from any part of the house by turning on a faucet in the bathtub. She would run to the room, leap into the tub and attempt to stop the drain with her paws, never tiring of this diversion as long as the water was running. Her insistence on swimming in the laundry tubs greatly retarded the progress of the washerwoman.

Like the tamed jaguarundi and ocelot, the domestic cat of some breeds becomes devoted exclusively to one person.

Like the tiger and some other large cats, the domestic cat is chagrined when it misses its goal.

It sympathizes with persons in distress, and several species of wild felines have been observed to do the same, though they would not approach a human being at any other time. Like the lynx and other small species of Felidæ, it arches its back when frightened. On hearing an interesting sound such as the gnawing of a mouse, its ears point like a lynx's. It hisses and spits like the jaguar and the tiger. It moves the tip of its tail in a wormlike manner and nearly all wild members of the genus *Felis* do the same.

Chapter Four

HOW LONG DOES IT TAKE A CAT TO BECOME FERAL?

How LONG it takes a cat to become feral depends largely upon the reason for its wildness and the conditions of its wild environment. If it has been forced to the woods because of human brutality, it is already partly wild and soon may become completely so. Where a cat has been abandoned accidentally in the wilderness and thus compelled to seek its own wild living, and the conditions are not too hostile, after two years of solitary existence it has shown an eagerness to make overtures to human beings and return to domestication.

New Englanders tell us that Angora cats at one time ran wild in the Maine woods, but because of their beauty they were reclaimed. There is no evidence that they had become wholly feral or that their reclamation was difficult even after several years of forest life. No doubt they found warm retreats during winter snows.

C. A. White tells of a cat named Jerry who sought human companionship at once when a boat landed at a place where he had been accidentally left when a camp broke up one year previously. He had not seen a human face in the interim, it was believed.

Climatic conditions appear to affect the rapidity with

which a cat becomes feral. When subjected to the hardships of continual low temperatures and insufficient shelter, it may become more quickly alienated from the desire for human friends. This is in keeping with the fact that the cat's temper is acidulated by repeated suffering of any kind which does not result from some natural condition such as teething, parturition, injuries sustained in conflicts with enemies or prey, etc.

Mr. H. E. Leavitt of San Francisco, California, has sent us his own observations of a case in point. He and a partner were in the Sierra Nevada Mountains, prospecting. One night, when the snow was about two feet deep, they heard the call of a cat which they thought was a wild cat (lynx) that had scented their poultry, and they decided to kill it. Every night it appeared on top of a boulder and uttered a distressed cry, and one moonlight night the two men set out with their guns; but when within firing range of the animal they were amazed to discover that it was no wild cat but a large domestic Maltese pussy. They captured it, took it to their cabin, petted and fed it; but it was nervous and fearful, and as soon as they were in their bunks escaped up the chimney, making a great noise as it dislodged some of the hot stones. The following night it appeared on the boulder again, uttering a heartrending wail, but permitted itself to be coaxed back to the cabin, where it was shown a hole cut in the door for its entrance and egress, and appeared to be satisfied. In the morning it was perched on the highest rafter, but came down for breakfast, now quite delighted with its new-found friends. For six months it lived with the men, always passing the night on the highest rafter, which it sought also if left alone during the day, as it evidently had been accustomed to resorting to tall trees for protection from pumas, lynxes, and coyotes. In the Sierra Nevadas eagles, hawks, and owls also prey on cats.

Later it was learned that the cat had been a city pet, taken from Oakland a year previously by a miner to a spot about five miles from the cabin. The man was killed by an explosion of dynamite and his body was not found for three months. The cat was forced to live for twelve months on such wild creatures as it could capture, such as birds, fish, mice, rats, squirrels, and gophers. Whether it was already in the neighborhood when the prospectors arrived and built their cabin, or whether it had traveled to the spot on hearing human beings about or smelling their cooking, is, of course, unknown.

T. S. Palmer, in 1898, wrote:

In one of the harbors of Kerguelen Island, southeast of the Cape of Good Hope, cats were allowed to run wild upon a little island known as Cat Island, which had been used as a wintering place for sealers for many years. Here they live in holes in the ground, preying upon sea birds and their young, and are said to have developed such extraordinary ferocity that it is almost impossible to tame them even when captured young.*

The account does not state how many years were required to produce complete wildness in the cats, whether they grew thick coats of fur to cope with the severity of the climate in winter, nor what changes they underwent physically in developing the necessary resistance to dampness. It rains on Cat Island three hundred days in the year and there is also much snow, though it does not remain long. The tem-

*The Danger of Introducing Noxious Animals and Birds. Yearbook of the U. S. Department of Agriculture for 1898, p. 87.

perature ranges from about 14° to 68° Fahr. Obviously the cats lived in holes in the ground only because there were no high places available, for it is certain that in cats thus left to their own resources the arboreal instinct comes into play very quickly, and they would not seek a low refuge if a high one could be found.

A friend of the author was obliged to leave her spayed black cat at her New Jersey bungalow for a week because the cat always interpreted the appearance of the automobile as an announcement of a return to town and hid herself; and on this occasion she could not be found. When the family returned for her, she was on the roof of the house.

Darwin noticed that in South America domestic cats which had taken to the woods and become feral increased in size and strength and changed color; and he took home from South America a domestic cat very much like a Kaffir cat. Others also have observed that those gone wild have taken on a gray coat and tabby markings—nature's way of revealing the original colors of their ancestors.

Chapter Five

ENEMIES OF THE CAT

WHEN ENEMIES of any of earth's creatures are under consideration, human beings, in nearly all instances, must be numbered first. Their cruel record in the treatment of the cat is extremely revolting.

Next to man, the most important enemies of the cat appear to be birds of prey. The wild cat and marten are said to constitute the favorite food of the golden eagle. The eagle has less pity for a cat than the cat has for a bird or mouse, and rarely indeed has a cat come off victor in conflict with this formidable foe. In one case, however, an eagle lost its life in attempting to kill a cat. An engineer owned a cat which was in the habit of riding on the front of the engine, where one day it was attacked by an eagle while the train was in motion. A fierce fight ensued, and the engineer, having blown his whistle in vain, started out on the running board with an iron bar to aid his pet; but the cat had already torn a large hole in the bird's neck, and when carried into the locomotive tender the eagle died in a few minutes. The cat, though bearing the scars of the battle, recovered.

Large owls occasionally prey upon cats, and a great horned owl recently carried off the pet cat of a forest ranger, descending to his porch for its prey.

A large hawk which attacked a kitten was vanquished by the mother cat in a terrible battle. "The cat lost an eye in the combat but killed the hawk and then ran to her bleeding kitten to care for its wounds."*

A cat is said also to have battled successfully with an alligator.

The mongoose kills kittens and is said to kill a cat with three bites.

A skunk once ate two kittens, but this probably was an exceptional case, for cats and skunks, in rural places, sometimes become greatly attached to one another and have been seen traveling about the woods together.

The raccoon and the weasel are sometimes named as enemies of the cat, but cats often kill weasels and in at least one instance a cat and a weasel became fast friends. Cats and raccoons also have developed into inseparable companions.

The lynx, puma, ocelot, and jaguarundi, though of the cat family, are said to destroy the domestic cat.

Vicious dogs, like their relatives, the foxes, coyotes, and wolves, are natural enemies of the cat, but any normal dog can easily be taught to love and protect the cats of the household.

Monkeys generally are referred to as enemies of cats, but they sometimes are seen in pet shops in cages with kittens which they are contentedly hugging (doubtless for warmth).

*Alfred H. Miles's *Natural History*, 1895.

PART TWO

PHYSIOLOGY AND PSYCHOLOGY OF THE CAT

Structure
Development
Longevity
Voice
Language
Brain
"Occult" Properties

Chapter Six

THE PHYSIOLOGY OF THE CAT

THE MUSCLES AND BONES

IN THE cat more than 500 voluntary muscles operate the supple body, and besides voluntary muscles, involuntary muscles are present, such as those of the alimentary canal, the bronchial tubes, the blood vessels, and the ureter. The muscles of the jaws are conspicuously large and strong, giving exceptional width to the zygomatic arches.

Tyndall's observations are said to have convinced him that the elasticity of the cat is only one tenth less than that of india-rubber, and Cuvier thought that the only development of strength to which the cat's organism does not lend itself is rapid running. That muscular development is more strongly pronounced in the male cat is illustrated by his ability to leap several times the length of his body in both upward and forward directions. We have seen one clear the hood of an automobile that was moving slowly, and we have also seen a tom cat leap a distance of eight feet in order to interpose himself at the crucial moment between a young protégé and a powerful adversary.

In the young cat over 300 bones may be numbered if we include the ear bones, the teeth, the chevron and sesamoid bones. If we omit these, there are about 233. In the aging cat the bones have a tendency to ankylose, two or more forming a mass and giving a somewhat shrunken appearance to a cat of twenty-one years or over, though the activities are not interfered with, and cats, however old, seldom lose the agility required in mousing. The skeleton is flexible, the spine's flexibility permitting of the rearing of the back and causing the domestic cat to appear to be stretching its bones as well as its muscles. The arrangement of levers in the limbs is the most remarkable in all the animal kingdom and explains in part the conspicuous suppleness of the feline, as well as its extraordinary agility and strength. It is these levers, the flexible spine, and the general perfection of the musculature which combine to produce in the cat an animal more graceful than the gazelle.

The number of vertebræ varies, according to the length of the tail, from about forty-eight to fifty-three. Generally they number about thirty in the back, seven of which are cervical, seven lumbar, three sacral, thirteen thoracic and connected with the thirteen pairs of ribs, and eighteen to twenty-three in the tail. As many as twenty-six caudal vertebræ have been counted.

The average length of the body, exclusive of tail, is eighteen inches in the female, twenty-one inches in the male. If the caudal appendage is included, many males measure three feet (from the tip of the nose to the tip of the tail). There are no dwarf cats in the Americas.*

THE FEET AND CLAWS

Cats are digitigrade (walking on their toes and soles) and the calcaneum or heel bone, though very well de-

*The frequently described dwarf cat of Paraguay does not exist. See p. 13.

veloped, is far back and does not touch the ground. Five toes, including the pollex or thumb, may be counted on the fore foot, four on the hind foot, each fitted with a claw; and cats with "double paws" are greatly prized world over. These **paws may carry six or more** toes, cats having been recorded with seven digits on both fore feet and six on both hind feet. This peculiarity, polydactylism, is known to be hereditary and may persist for a number of generations. At their tips the bones of a cat's claws turn upward, preventing the claws from touching the ground and producing a noiseless tread.

The cat manipulates its "hands" much after the fashion of the anthropoids and can use one claw to hook a passing object such as the coat of a person whose attention it desires to attract. The "hands" are used to test the temperature of liquids and the character of strange objects; to wash the face and head; to raise food to the mouth (some cats always eat from their paws and never from a dish); to dip into a receptacle containing food, after which they are licked off; to stun and capture rodents; to secure a hold upon a bone or chunk of meat; and to draw down the upper branches of an enticing plant such as catnip. They are used to play with leaves and other objects, and in fighting, and for many other purposes. (See chapter on Voice and Language, also Psychology.)

The pads, which are extremely sensitive, are formed of tissue fiber and fat, and protect the bones on which the weight of the animal rests. They are rough and hairless and consist of one under each nail and a large central one called trilobed and shaped a little like a clover leaf. An extra pad on the fore foot is situated almost directly over the pisiform bone in the wrist, giving a total of seven pads on the fore foot and but five on the hind foot.

The claws are curved and sharp for the purpose of tearing flesh, and are so formed as to facilitate the progress of the animal in walking on steep or dangerous surfaces which permit of their being protracted to form a grasping organ.

The feet are not adapted to rapid running or rough or prolonged walking, and in homing, when a cat walks many miles to return to a loved abode, it sometimes arrives with painfully sore feet.

The feet still hold some mystery in the use made of them when the cat makes an upward double leap, the first against a fence half way to the top where there is nothing to which the claws may cling, and the second from there to the top; and when it descends a smooth, perpendicular board and maintains its equilibrium. A fine sense of balance appears to be a more important aid in these feats than the structure of the paws.

When the cat rears on its haunches for short periods the weight is rested on the pads and toes; when for longer periods the tibia are flexed to support much of the weight, while the remainder is distributed over pads, toes, and metatarsus, the entire foot being set down plantigrade fashion; and the fore legs are held in various positions, above and below the head.

It still is commonly believed that cats scratch trees and other wooden objects to sharpen their claws, though this theory was rejected by scientists many years ago. Charles Darwin (*Naturalist's Voyage Round the World,* 1871) noticed that they scratch to tear off the ragged points of the claws as these are being shed, and Ole N. de Weerdt has

Ginger belongs collectively to the Farmers' Market of Jenkintown, Pa. His curly tail illustrates the manner in which mutations arise in the animal kingdom.

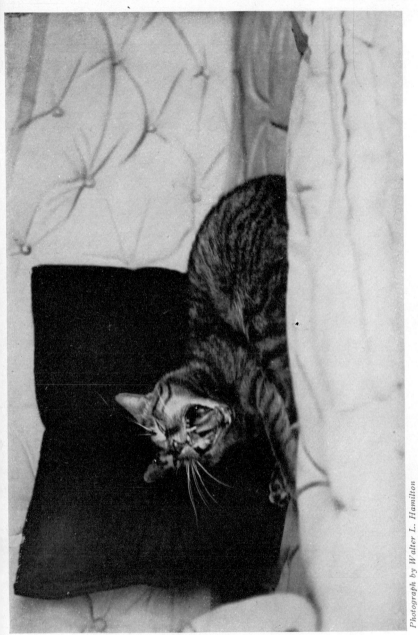

Photograph by Walter L. Hamilton

The adult dentition consists of thirty teeth, and when the cat yawns it shows them all.

observed that they use the rough bark of trees always much softer than their claws, and after scratching the claws into the surface, make a circular stroke, pulling first downward and then outward and slightly upward. Cats also use rugs and other fabrics for this purpose. They remove the loose bits of the hind claws with their teeth. Wild felines select one tree for repeated use, possibly in order to avoid attracting the attention of other animals, enemies and prey. The shedding of the claws is not seasonal, but occurs throughout the year.

THE HAIR, WHISKERS AND EYEBROWS

Hairless cats have been exhibited, principally the New Mexican breed, but most cats have a thick covering of hair except on the nose, pads, and nipples. It is said that the Mombas cat of Africa has very short, stiff hair with a few long hairs above the eyes that form eyebrows, but no eyelashes. Long-haired cats may have a thick furry undercoat and a silky top coat, or the coat may be uniform from root to tip. In black cats the hair turns gray with age, and in Siamese cats the mask pales from illness and sorrow. Grayness may occur as early as at fifteen years. Miss Annie A. Chadbourne of West Andover, Massachusetts, tells us that her tiger-and-white cat, Billy, who lived to be eighteen years old, "showed gray in the black on the top of his shoulders and over his eyes several years before the end."

The vibrissæ—the long, coarse hairs projecting from the muzzle and above the eyes—are sense organs of great delicacy, the bulbs of which are copiously supplied with blood vessels and nerves. They communicate to the cat the nature of its surroundings in the dark, though probably not, as is commonly believed, a knowledge as to whether or not its body will pass through an aperture, for slender cats sometimes have long vibrissæ, while fat cats may have short ones. They are used also as organs of communication between individuals, friendly when two cats that love each other or wish to become acquainted touch whiskers, unfriendly when two altercating toms do the same. These vibrissæ, which number from twenty-five to thirty, are arranged in four rows, the two middle rows being longest.

The coat is shed in spring, summer, and early fall.

When the animal is frightened the hair of its back and tail stands on end.

BRAIN, NERVES AND TAIL

A study of the brain of the cat has given many celebrated anatomists much of their knowledge of the human brain, so closely does it resemble ours in miniature.

The cat's brain is a direct continuation of its spinal cord, greatly enlarged, and consists of a large cerebrum and smaller cerebellum. It is composed of two kinds of matter, gray and white, the gray being made up largely of cells, the white of fibers, and the arrangement of the folds of the cerebellum provides for an increase in the amount of its gray matter.

Twelve pairs of cranial nerves arise from the medulla oblongata, and there are about thirty-eight or forty pairs of spinal nerves. In some cats the entire body is so sensitive that they cannot endure being touched. Sense organs of pain are present in every organ of the body. Yet despite the great delicacy of its nervous system and its extremely nervous temperament, a cat seldom suffers from nervous diseases.

The tail has lost its reputation as a balancing power, since tailless cats balance as well as others; but as a continuation of the spine it is a sensitive organ of mute communication. It has a language of its own. Harrison Weir tells of a cat, Fritz, whose tail was so sensitive that he could not bear to have it handled or even referred to. If any one pointed to it and said "Tail," he growled, and if this were repeated, he left the room. A two-months-old male kitten which the author examined for its rugæ cried when any part of its body was touched.

Cats' tails may be long and straight, long and kinked, short and kinked, short and knobbed, bobbed, curled, double or missing. In the Philippine Islands, for example, the cats' tails show the kink characteristic of the cats throughout southeastern Asia. Tailless and bobtailed cats have arisen as sports, but as there is no taillessness in the ancient ancestors of cats at present known to science, nor in any extant species of wild cat, and the bobtailed condition often is due to a failure of the bones to develop, neither phenomenon is attributed to a reversion to type. Oddities in cats' tails, such as truncated tails, double tails and curly tails, seen world over, furnish excellent examples of the manner in which mutations arise throughout the animal kingdom. Curly-tailed cats were found in China in the twelfth century, and like bobtailed and double-tailed cats they have been found in the United States. That some of these odd traits become fixed over large areas is illustrated by the wide range of kinktailed and stump-tailed cats, already mentioned.

PURRING LIGAMENTS

The purr, which, as Heinrich Heine says, is each cat's

own "flute and viol," may be gentle and inaudible except when the ear is applied to the cat's body, or it may be so violent as to make the cat cough and be perceptible twelve feet away, in which case the ribs vibrate like a stringed instrument. The whirr of a spinning wheel is said to resemble it. The purr nearly always is an expression of the pleasurable emotions, but Margery Bianco and others have called attention to the fact that a cat in pain or distress will give a hoarse, sharp purr.

When in deep slumber the cat ceases to purr, but recommences on waking up or if conscious of the approach or touch of a loved human being.

How the cat effects its purr is a question which long has perplexed physiologists, who have called certain prominent ligaments or folds of membrane on either side of the larynx the superior or false vocal cords and the inferior or true vocal cords, assuming that the cat vibrates the former to produce the purr, while the latter are regulated to produce the various inflections of voice.

HEART, BLOOD AND LUNGS

The cat's heart is small and ovoid and made up of right and left auricles and ventricles. The aorta springs from its base, and the blood is said to make a complete circuit of the body in sixteen seconds.

Under excitement the cat develops an excess of adrenalin and sugar in the blood, and the action of its stomach becomes interrupted. In its heart-beats the animal is inconstant, as in its respiration, temperature, period of gestation, and other physical characters. The heart-beats normally number from

110 to 160 a minute, and may be plainly felt by pressing on the left side of the thoracic cavity; or pulsation may be taken at the radial artery on the upper, inner side of the fore leg, inside the lower jaw, or at the femoral artery on the inner side of the thigh.

The normal temperature runs from about 100° to 102°.

The lungs are much lobed, the right one being slightly larger than the left, and the cat coughs, sneezes and yawns (all respiratory functions). Its normal respiration is from twenty to thirty a minute.

FACIAL EXPRESSIONS

The cat's large variety of facial expressions is not equaled by those of any other animal save man. They convey pleasure, amusement, pain, perplexity, mischief, fright, interrogation, expectancy, triumph, grief, and other emotions. Cats frown when annoyed and sometimes assume a sweet expression when talked to. A cat will put on a very sweet face when a loved child picks it up, and the expression of the female generally is somewhat softer than that of the male. The face is a certain guide to the manner of life of the cat and instantly reveals the character of its home, particularly in the expression of the eyes, the glance of the well-treated cat being mild and trustful, while that of the ill-used cat is hard and suspicious.

Under emotional stress the cat acts much like the human being, outwardly as well as inwardly. It trembles, its heartbeats quicken, its pupils widen, and its features express its feelings. The cat's ears also are indices to its state of mind, pointing forward with joy and backward with disapproval.

Kittens and young cats sometimes smile, while older cats smirk by the hour.*

NOSE AND MOUTH

A small, broad nose, differently colored in different breeds and sometimes changing color with age, furnishes one of the striking characteristics of the domestic feline. In a healthy cat the nose is cool and moist. In a troubled cat the nose becomes wrinkled and abbreviated.

Animals in which the nether lip is shorter than the over lip are adapted to lapping, and the cat can make a spoon out of its tongue in imbibing milk and other liquids. When excessively hot it opens its mouth and pants. In a healthy cat the saliva is free from bacteria. The rough pink tongue is covered with minute papillæ of four different kinds and is adapted to working meat off bones, also to reaching and cleaning every part of the body except the back of the neck and the space between the shoulders. As Leigh Hunt observed, "She fetches amazing tongues at her hind hips!"

Hard and soft palates form the roof of the mouth, the hard palate lying at the front and being marked by curved, transverse corrugations or ridges known as rugæ, between which are rows of papillæ. Though the roof of the mouth commonly is pink, it may be pigmented if there is much black in the coat.

The rugæ number most frequently seven in the male

---

*The loose skin and sinuous body of the cat, and its great variety of facial expressions were for centuries the despair of painter and sculptor, and until the invention of the camera the animal seldom was truthfully represented. Every great artist tried his hand at portraying it, but not half a dozen succeeded, and the majority soon abandoned the attempt.

and six or seven in the female, but may number five, eight, or nine. In fifty cats and kittens, long-haired, and domestic and foreign short-haired, in which the rugæ have been counted by or for the author, they numbered as follows:

2 (males)	had 9
3 (2 males, 1 female)	had 8
6 (5 males, 1 female)	had 5
14 (2 males, 12 females)	had 6
25 (12 males, 13 females)	had 7

Inasmuch as the Chinese are said to believe that cats having nine rugæ are the best ratters, it is interesting to note that the only ones examined which had that number were two domestic short-haired males.

It is quite certain that the number in the mouth of the kitten is the number it will carry through life, as we found seven in female kittens but three weeks old.

No studies have been made to ascertain whether the number of rugæ is hereditary, or whether it is correlated with some other physical trait. It may differ only because of differences in the rugæ of various species of wild ancestors.

The milk dentition, which is fully established in about four weeks after birth, consists of twenty-six teeth, and some kittens cut their teeth, as some also open their eyes, much earlier than others. Our observations showed that at three weeks only the incisors and canines had been cut, though molars and premolars could be felt through the swollen gums, and at three weeks and three days the canines felt sharp and the entire first set of teeth was in place. The deciduous teeth are shed at between four and seven months, sometimes a little later, and some cat fanciers then call the kitten a cat, others calling it a cat at nine months. Of course, it is not a cat until it is sexually mature.

The adult dentition consists of thirty teeth and when the cat yawns it shows them all. In the upper jaws there are on each side three incisors, one canine, three premolars and one molar. In the lower jaw there are three incisors, one canine, two premolars and one molar on each side. The teeth are fitted for cutting and tearing.

KIDNEYS, BLADDER AND GLANDS

The kidneys are bean-shaped and the bladder pear-shaped. A gall bladder also is present, as well as pancreas and liver, the liver, which is large, lying on the right side because of the position of the stomach. The animal possesses salivary glands and its full complement of ductless or endocrine glands, including spleen, thyroid, and thymus glands; but the thymus, which is present in the kitten, later disintegrates and is nearly or wholly wanting in the cat.

STOMACH AND INTESTINES

The stomach is pear-shaped, its long axis being curved in the shape of an almost perfect semicircle. In the three-months-old kitten its capacity is one tablespoon, in the adult cat four and one-half ounces or more. The cat's generous digestive space permits of taking large supplies of food and resisting the demands of a long famine. It can go for six days without food with no serious results; but by the thirteenth day it has lost ninety-seven per cent of its fat. Cats have existed for an even longer time without sustenance, as in the case of one named Thomas Cadillac, who was accidentally shipped with a chassis from Detroit, Michigan, to Sydney, Australia, on the *Trevalgen* in 1921. (Contemporary accounts stated that he imbibed some grease and oiled paper from the engine and fifty pages of the instruction book.*) When the packing case was opened seven weeks later the cat was in a state of coma, but was revived in a veterinary hospital and lived to become quite celebrated, though his features always bore a melancholy look.

The small intestine is about three times the length of the body, the large intestine about one-half the body length, so that in a cat whose body measures twenty-four inches the intestines are about seven feet long. The digestive system is comparatively simple, and as there is no vermiform appendix, nuts and other strange new items in the fare cannot cause appendicitis. The cat's body, like ours, consists largely of water, and therefore requires internal moisture.

THE WEIGHT

The weight differs greatly in cats, as in other animals, even in those of the same breed reared under the same conditions. The weight of the kitten at birth averages 3.21 to 3.95 ounces, but may be less than three ounces or more than four, and up to six months cat breeders consider that it should be about one pound for each month. The average weight of an adult male is from nine to seventeen pounds, of an adult female from six to ten pounds. The weight commonly decreases with age and an old male will shrink from seventeen pounds to eight, or from twelve pounds to five.

*The Literary Digest, July 2, 1921.

We have authenticated cases of cats weighing from twenty-one to twenty-eight pounds, and unverified reports of some of heavier weights, even thirty-four and thirty-five pounds; but if the latter figures are correct these cats are in a class with those that live for more than thirty years. Mrs. Edith W. Berwyn of San Diego, California, owns a Persian red tabby neuter male, Ginger, who weighs twenty-three pounds. Miss Verry Packard of Brooklyn, New York, owned Tommy Atkins, a tiger-and-white male cat weighing twenty-one pounds, also Honeysuckle Pansyblossom Snowball, an orange-and-white neuter male who reached a weight of twenty-eight pounds. Cats weighing twenty-five pounds have been exhibited at cat shows.

THE SENSES

Touch. The cat has the most delicate sense of touch in the animal kingdom. Every hair is sensitive, not only to concrete objects but to the elements, and a drop of water touching even the rough pads of the feet sends a nervous shock to the brain. A kitten will smell and pat a flower without injuring a petal, and we often hear of cats that tread in and out among a valuable collection of glassware including thin-stemmed goblets, overturning nothing.*

Taste. The sense of taste is not so keen as in the monkey, and as a rule cats cannot distinguish food which has been poisoned. They will not eat carrion like a dog, preferring their meat stuffs fresh, but to test the freshness of meat they rely on the sense of smell. Tastes of individuals differ widely.

*To the best of our knowledge these are male cats, or females that have their liberty. See Moods and Emotions, p. 156.

Hearing. Sir Francis Galton (*Human Faculty,* 1883) says: "Of all creatures I have found none superior to cats in the power of hearing shrill sounds. It is perfectly remarkable what a faculty they have in this way."

The cat's ears quickly detect sounds entirely beyond the human range, and their sharp hearing is attributed to the large auditory bulla, which increase the resonance of sounds and enable the cat to detect the difference in those much alike, and also to distinguish half tones, to which other animals are deaf. Doctor Ernest G. Wever of Princeton University discovered that cats can detect tones as high as 20,000 cycles a second. (The human voice ranges no more than 5000 cycles.)* That the hearing is more acute in some cats than in others is illustrated by the following facts: Some cats on board an Australian vessel always hurried to the deck at the sound of a flying fish falling upon it, but never appeared when the sailors attempted to imitate the peculiar flop made by the fishes as they fell. (Mrs. Mary Pamela Milne-Home to the author.) A cat owned by Miss Linda M. French of Staten Island, New York, Catiline by name, whose favorite food was an egg, preferably boiled, "would appear," says Miss French, "from nowhere at any sound that remotely suggested the cracking of an eggshell."

We have some authenticated instances of cats that were able to distinguish the family car from all other cars, apparently by some slight difference in the sound of the engine.

Examples: Mrs. H. R. Merrill of Brooklyn, New York, keeps her car in a garage diagonally across the street from her home,

*Science, February 21, 1930.

where another car also is kept. Henri, her long-haired cat, always went to meet her when she drove into the garage and never mistook the other car for hers.

Mrs. Thomas I. Miller of Staten Island, New York, tells us that some neighbors took their cat to ride in a new car. It became frightened, leapt out, and refused to return when they called it. They remembered that it knew the engine of the old car, went home, took out the old car and drove to the spot where the cat had escaped. They called, and the cat came briskly to them.

Mrs. Walter L. Hamilton of Holyoke, Massachusetts, had a cat, Peggy, who climbed a telephone pole, and when she heard the family car approaching descended to be taken in for the ride home.

Cats also distinguish the different bells in the home—front door, rear door, telephone, etc., and develop an intimate knowledge of footsteps.

It is believed that the semicircular canals of the ear in the cat do not concern hearing, since these canals are well developed in the fish, which is deaf. The fish is believed to use the canals in balancing itself and also in sensing vibrations, and probably their use in the cat is the same. In conjunction with the testing of the elements by her hair, pussy may derive her foreknowledge of earthquakes through these semicircular canals, which doubtless are responsible also for the ability of the tailless cat to balance itself perfectly and of the falling cat to right itself; and possibly for the cat's ability to negotiate a perpendicular board without losing its balance. They are evidently present in the deaf cat. (See p. 70.)

The correlation between deafness and blue eyes, occurring in some white cats, remains one of the physiological mysteries of the domestic feline. Kittens in general being both blue-eyed and deaf at birth, one theory suggested that if they retained the blue eyes they also retained the deafness; but this proved unsound inasmuch as many blue-eyed white cats hear perfectly, and hearing commonly develops in kittens within a few days after birth while the eyes may remain blue for several weeks or months. (See chapter on Development of the Kitten.) Nevertheless, some having odd eyes have been thought to hear on the side with the blue eye, and cases are on record in which blue-eyed kittens were deaf until three months old, when the blue of the iris began to deepen into yellow and hearing was established. Deafness does not occur in Siamese cats, which also are partial albinos and retain their blue eyes through life, and it does not occur in pure albinos. Some deaf cats develop an extraordinary keenness in sensing vibrations and their deafness often is hardly noticeable, but Mrs. Henry Simon of Centereach, New York, a breeder of white Persian cats, informs us that hers are restless and closely on the watch for approaching objects. She considers their carefulness a strong protection. She is certain also that odd-eyed cats hear equally well on the side with the blue eye. The condition is apparently hereditary, and though no effort has been made in this direction, it is highly probable that as deafness in the blue-eyed white cat is a recessive trait, it could be bred out by using only hearing cats with hearing forebears in the breeding stock.

Sight. Cats use their eyes a great deal more than do dogs. Experiments made in Germany on the effects of motion pictures upon various animals established the fact that though the response of dogs is practically nil, three-fifths of the cats respond actively, showing fight when a large dog appears on the screen. The cat's discrimination of form and color appears to be imperfect. Everyone has seen a cat arch its back at sight of some unfamiliar object and noticed that, impelled by curiosity, it cautiously approaches. If the object stirs, the cat leaps away, but if it remains motionless the cat smells it first, then perhaps touches it with its paw to determine its nature, and no longer takes the slightest interest in it.

Though cats cannot see in absolute darkness, their vision in a faint light is much better than that of most animals. The dusk, the starlight, the moonlight, find them very active and happy. Their eyes catch half lights invisible to us, and the pupil is sensitive to ultra-violet rays beyond our range. The epithelial rods of the retina contain a large amount of visual purple, and this purple, which enables the animal to see in near darkness, is known to be strongly linked with Vitamin A.

The pupil varies in size and form according to the amount of light. It is capable of great expansion, which may be observed under the stress of emotion as well as at night and in cloudy weather. Its widening circle admits the faint rays of night, and when contracted into a vertical slit it shuts out all excess light of day, permitting of very exact vision under either extreme.* The cat's good vision makes it an excellent judge of distance and in leaping it seldom misses its goal.

*From the vertical-pupil effect of certain kinds of oriental chrysoberyl and occidental quartz when cut *en cabochon,* they are called "cat's eyes." These gems reveal a line of light across their rounded domes. The stony operculum of a species of trochid of the Fijian Islands presents an open-eye effect and is also called "cat's eye," the large pupil being green and the iris brown, with a white sclerotic.

The pupil is not smallest at high noon, as is commonly believed, but contracts in an extremely bright light at any time of day. At two o'clock and later, if the day is bright, it is equally as small as at noon.

The pupil varies in shape with age, being a pointed oval in the young cat and round in the older cat, with many intermediate stages. At present there is no method of arriving at a cat's age, but in time a way may be found of approximating it by studying the pupil, with respect to both size and shape.

Unlike dogs and many other animals the cat is able to gaze fixedly into the human eye. Its expressive, forward-looking eyes have a compelling power, and they shine in near darkness when rays of light strike the tapetum lucidum. This is of a metallic yellowish blue, green, or red. If on a bright night edibles are thrown from an upper window to cats in a yard below, pairs of lights of different colors may be seen directed upward, or one eye may show one color and the other another, according to the angle at which the light strikes them. In the Siamese cat, in which the iris is only slightly pigmented, the pupil reflects a fiery glow in near darkness or under excitement.

The iris is said to change color during excitement, and in sickness rich amber eyes have been observed to fade into a dull green and the blue eyes of the Siamese into a pale opal.

Laboratory experiments made on cats to determine the extent of their color blindness have had quite opposite results. Some appear to possess a good discrimination of color, others act like persons affected with dichromatic vision (*i.e.*, those with blue-green or red blindness), confusing white with yellow, and red, green, blue, and violet with gray, though in some experiments the cats distinguished blue from light gray and black. They do not confuse yellow, orange, or red-orange with gray, and this is believed to be because of the brightness of these colors. One theory, therefore, is that cats observe intensities rather than colors. We suspect this might be modified to read, _"In a bright light_ some cats appear to observe intensities rather than colors."

Perhaps the cat is color-blind by daylight though not in a faint light, for a piece of meat falling on the grass or pavement, though found with difficulty in a bright light, is readily seen at dusk or in the night when faint lights are falling from the windows; and its color-blindness may produce its form-blindness, for its daytime vision is obviously partly dependent on motion. If the meat in the grass were to move, the cat would perceive it in the brightest light. It can see a sparrow moving in the grass when the bird, if motionless, is difficult even for human eyes to discern. It has been thought that the variation in the size of the pupil may serve to keep the retina in twilight and that the cat lives in a gray world like ours at dusk. We suspect, however, that its world becomes bright and colorful when daylight fades, but if it does live in a twilight world, motion naturally would be an important aid to vision.

We have authenticated instances of cats showing a preference for a certain color, irrespective of the nature of the object or the material so colored. Napoleon the Weather Prophet (described more particularly in the chapter on "Telepathy and Occult Vision") was attracted by anything that was blue, favored blue goods without respect to their texture, and died on a blue blanket. A cat named Harriet, belonging to Miss Florence Carter of Oneida, New York, is similarly fond of red and, like Napoleon, wishes to dispose herself on materials dyed her favorite color.*

The cat, using its eyes before its nose, sometimes is deceived by unfamiliar apparel worn by its friends and avoids them. Bob, a cat owned by Miss Leora Wilson of Canisteo, New York, did not recognize Miss Wilson's brother when, after a year's absence, he returned in a different garb; but when he donned old, familiar garments the cat remembered him and ran to him. Harriet (Carter) was fond of a young lady who was staying at her home, but when the girl appeared in a ski suit, the cat, though appearing to recognize her voice, became alarmed and ran away.

Smell. The sense of smell, though much more delicate than ours, is called less keen than the dog's, but whereas the dog loves the odor of carrion, the cat is sensitive to perfumes, such as cologne, lavender water, hand lotions, etc., and many cats love the fragrance of certain flowers such as heliotrope and violets. Their passion for smelling (and eating) catnip, valerian, patchouli, silver vine (*Actinidia polygama*), and other plants is well known, though some cats dislike some or all of these. A cat owned by the author hated the odor of catnip and such of her kittens as were observed hated it also, but whether cats have an inherited dislike for certain odors is not known.

Normal cats know instantly from a distance of many

---

*This cat leaps upon an ironing board where red goods are being pressed and resents any attempt to dislodge her unless some other material colored red, such as an apron or shawl, is spread on a chair, in which case she accepts the transfer. She dislikes being held, but will jump on any one's lap if the person is wearing a garment with red in it.

feet whether another cat is a male or female, and without doubt this is due to their keen perception of bodily odors. They are perplexed by their first encounter with a gelded cat, and the latter does not recognize any difference in the sexes. His sense of smell is not dulled by castration, but sex odors are without significance to him.

Certain odors such as those of bitter almonds and rue are said to be highly distasteful to the majority of cats, and rue formerly was tied under the wings of domestic fowl to prevent cats from preying upon them.

So discriminating is the cat's sense of smell that an odor to which the nostrils have been applied, even the (to us) soft fragrance of facial cream, may seem pungent to it; then it opens its mouth and breathes thus for a moment to rest the offended nasal passages.

THE FALLING CAT TURNS OVER

It is common knowledge that even within the space of a foot or less a cat held back down and released will land on its feet. Motion pictures taken of a falling cat and described by Crabtree demonstrate that it first contracts its fore legs and then turns its fore part round; next it contracts its hind legs, extends the fore legs, and gives the hind part a turn. By this continued action it turns itself through any required angle, though at no time has it any angular momentum about its "axis." Muller and Weed found that if the cat is blindfolded it still turns over, but makes its landing less accurately. The ability to turn appears to depend upon the semicircular canals of the ear, and these evidently are present also in the deaf cat. Mrs. Henry Simon has kindly made the turns-in-falling test for us and reports that both deaf and hearing blue-eyed white cats make the turn perfectly and land on all four feet when released back down at a distance of from twelve to eighteen inches from the ground.

Miss Merlys Blakeslee tells us that her ocelot, Saba, when held back down three feet above a couch and released, turned over. It seems likely, therefore, that most species of felines which live largely in trees turn over in falling and land on their feet.

The cat's spine, though flexible, is easily broken, and it does not leap from great heights except when in danger. A stray cat, when frightened, jumped from the roof of a house twenty-eight feet to the ground and walked away unhurt; a cat, finding itself on a strange fire escape, leapt forty feet to the ground and suffered no apparent injury; but some cats are injured or killed by lesser falls. Tiger, a gray-and-white cat owned by Miss Sarah Hurd of Oneida, New York, fell off the roof of a one-story house and was paralyzed. Beatrice Portinari, a cat owned by the author, died from internal injuries sustained in a fall from an apartment-house window about thirty-five feet from the ground. Isaac, a black short-haired cat belonging to Mr. Thomas W. Rutherford of Brooklyn, New York, "fell from a housetop seventy-five feet to the concrete steps below," says Mr. Rutherford, "and only broke one of his nails and knocked his breath out; but Fluffy, a fine Angora, did the same and was killed." The keeping of cats in the upper stories of office buildings and printing houses has been largely abandoned because of their facility for falling out of a window and being killed.

ELECTRICITY OF THE CAT

Some nervous and sensitive persons declare that the electricity emitted by a cat gives them a pleasant thrill. It is believed to be more apparent in cold weather, though on a crisp fall day a cat passing quickly through dry brush has been observed to blaze a trail of blue light.*

Electricity resides in the skins of great cats and small, and it is said that a rod of glass or sealing wax rubbed with a cat skin will become charged with static electricity.

Though black cats are reputed to be the most electric, those tested by and for the author, both short-haired and long-haired, had less electricity than cats of other colors; but climatic conditions may have had some bearing on these cases. The fur of some long-haired black cats tested for electricity was heard to crackle though no shock was felt; but the electric shock given by two shaded silver Persians and a red Persian owned by Mrs. Edith W. Berwyn of San Diego, California, was so great that Mrs. Berwyn was unable to keep her hands on the animals.

To obtain an electric shock the left palm is placed on the cat's throat with thumb and middle finger pressing lightly on the scapulæ (shoulder bones), then the right hand is drawn down the back. The shock is felt in the left hand. Exactly how much the current varies with individuals is not known. The cat itself appears to be unaware of it, although Mrs. Virginia R. Cobb, in testing her Siamese cats for

*Some people are similarly electric. The author once saw a woman walk across a floor, shuffling her feet on the carpet to produce friction, then raise her arm toward a metal bar while electric sparks flew from her finger-tips.

electricity at our request, found that though they gave no shock they purred madly.

THE FAT OF THE CAT

The adipose tissue, called also fat tissue, consists of vesicles filled with oily matter; and the nervous tissue contains fatty matters which, according to Mivart, are made up of cerebrin, glyco-phosphoric and palmitic acids, olein, cholesterin, and margarin (which is a mixture of stearin and palmitin). Under starvation the fat of the cat sustains it for a number of days.

THE REPRODUCTIVE SYSTEM

The male: The testes normally descend into the scrotum at about the time of birth or soon after, and sexual maturity is reached in from nine to twelve months. Breeding males in catteries are known as studs, and males in general are considered best for mating at from three to fourteen years, but they have been known to breed at six months, and, as shown in the chapter on Longevity, until their twenty-fifth year. The breeding age, however, may depend on breed and climate.

Males which have not been castrated are retromingent (spraying backward). After castration they are no longer retromingent, probably because of paralysis of the muscles. The fluid they spray when not castrated, however, is not always from the kidneys (or bladder). Frequently it is an alkaline viscid secretion emanating from Cowper's bulbo-urethral glands (two small bodies characteristic of male mammals and which in the cat are about the size of a pea). It has been suggested that this secretion may be for the purpose of neutralizing any acidity of the urethra which might inhibit the activity of the spermatozoa, and inasmuch as Cowper's glands cease to function after castration, this theory seems plausible. It is believed that the glands atrophy after castration. In veterinary anatomy Cowper's glands, though considerably larger than the prostate glands, are called the "small prostates" because their fluid has the same physical properties as the prostate glands and is believed to be secreted at the same time. It is also secreted at other times, however, even immediately after mating. Its pungent odor is obnoxious in catteries and entails considerable labor in keeping the males' cages clean. A cat will spray when jealous and offended (see p. 158), and perhaps the fluid from these glands is also used by the cat as a notice to other males of his presence, or by a poor fighter as a symbol of temporary victory, or to represent some other purely masculine activity.

Possible example: The author witnessed a singular instance of the use of what probably was this fluid. A small black cat had been busy driving other cats away from a clump of neglected shrubs where she had one kitten about two days old, when suddenly she was seen reposing near by in an abandoned hammock —certain evidence that the kitten was dead. A large black-and-white tom cat who was very fond of her and had washed her face and ears before the kitten came, entered the yard, saw her in the hammock, went to look at the nest, immediately climbed into the hammock, kissed her and departed. Another tom cat, a yellow specimen, came, saw her in the hammock, went to see the dead kitten, *sprayed the spot* and left the yard. The latter cat frequently had been beaten in a fracas with the former tom, but on this occasion the idea of fighting did not occur to either male. Now, if we knew why the yellow cat sprayed the nest containing the dead kitten and were certain that the fluid he sprayed was the secretion from his Cowper's glands, we might know the purpose (or one purpose) of Cowper's glands. If we knew who or what killed the kitten, it would help still more.

The female: The female cat matures, as a rule, at from five to eight months, but in some cases not for a year, and she may begin to breed at six months or not for two years. In one case known to the author a cat that never had kittened began to breed when eight years old, producing one family a year for several years. Breeding females in catteries are known as queens, and queens in general are held to be in their prime when between two and eight years old, though it is not uncommon for them to breed up to twelve or fourteen years.

They come in season for from three to fifteen days about three times a year, though in the tropics four times, and if not mated the periods may last for three weeks or longer. If a mother cat loses her young, she will sometimes mate again almost immediately. In the latitude of New York the female cat breeds twice, sometimes three times, during the warmer months, mating from about the first of February to the end of May or later. By her cry or "calling" males are apprised of her condition, but more particularly by her odor, to which, like male insects toward the females of their species, they are drawn from hundreds of feet away. During the period of œstrum the cat mews and caterwauls like any male, becomes agitated, crouches with hind legs flexed, and her eyes become bleared.

The duration of gestation ranges from fifty-five to sixty-nine days, most often being sixty-two and one-half; and this wide variation doubtless is due to past matings with wild cats of various species in which the period of gestation differed from that of the long-domesticated breed. The uterus of the cat is bifid, and the ovum scarcely visible to the unaided eye, being from about 1/180th to 1/120th of an inch in diameter.

It is well known that cats are promiscuous, *i.e.,* both polyandrous and polygamous, each having as many mates as the neighborhood affords, but we have noticed that females favor certain males and select them for mating first, receiving others afterward; also, that after mating the males settle in a circle about the female and do not quarrel, and this occurs every day during the period of œstrum until they discover that her period is over. Then they cry almost constantly for twenty-four hours, whether she has been in heat for three days or longer; but what the reason may be for this phenomenon, we have been unable to discover. The crying gradually ceases and strange males attracted to the neighborhood disperse.

When pregnant, the cat, however intelligent, does not consider the space through which her body may safely pass, and a cat in kitten has been known to kill her entire litter and sometimes herself by forcing her way through an aperture much too small.

Though parturition frequently is easy, it may prove agonizing or even fatal. Cæsarian operations sometimes are performed upon high-bred cats and no doubt many domestic short-haired cats have lost their lives in great suffering for want of similar attention. After cutting the umbilical cord the mother cat eats the placenta, and if the enclosing amniotic membrane is not broken the kitten will suffocate. The birth fluid is phosphorous and one man, observing a new-born kitten in the dark, reported that it appeared luminous.

When the birth is difficult the cat will readily accept alcoholic liquors, and one mother cat will assist another who needs obstetrical aid, whether they are on friendly terms or not, by working with her tongue in an effort to press the kitten forth. In a case described to the author by Miss Violet M. Turner of New York City a desperately sick cat accepted the services of a dog of the household, who broke the enveloping membrane of the kittens as they were born and washed them thoroughly. (This dog, an Airedale bitch, had whelped.)

Four pairs of teats or nipples are present in the cat, though five pairs also occur, and each nipple has eight or ten orifices.

Where cats are permitted to breed as frequently as they wish, the young most often number from four to eight in a litter, the first and last litters being small. We have a record of one domestic short-haired cat that produced five kittens, then three, then one every year for some years. Some cats never produce more than one kitten at a birth, but Siamese queens sometimes bring forth eight or nine young, one having given birth to ten, another to eleven, and a third to twelve.

Mrs. Eva T. Harris of Van Nuys, California, who has bred blue and black Persians for thirty years, believes that continuous breeding of long-haired cats tends to increase the number of kittens in each litter, but decreases the quality of the stock for exhibition purposes. If breeding is restricted during the first two or three years, she finds that the queens will ask for but one litter a year, and one of her Persian queens gave the best kittens after she had passed her twelfth birthday.

The number of kittens a cat commonly bears in her life-time varies greatly even within a given number of years. Miss Linda M. French estimates that her domestic short-haired cat, Snowball, who lived to be about ten years old, produced between seventy and eighty kittens. Mrs. Virginia R. Cobb tells us that her Siamese queen, Chinkaling, thirteen years old, has produced ninety-one kittens.

Although one hundred and twenty has been suggested as the probable maximum, a seventeen-year-old cat owned by Miss Joan Dare of San Francisco has produced not less than 135 kittens, and a cat that bred at from two to twenty-eight years had more than two hundred kittens. (See p. 99.)

The litters of many Persian cats number five or six kittens, and if permitted they would produce from fifteen to eighteen young a year. Mrs. A. E. Townsend of Ardsley, New York, whose silver Persians are restricted to breeding once a year, sends us the record of three queens, Champion Silver Frills, the daughter of this cat, Bonnie Lass O'Balloch Myle, and the granddaughter, Double Champion Bonnie Thistle Beauty. Champion Silver Frills had but seventeen kittens over a period of twelve years, her daughter produced but twenty-four in six years of breeding, and the grand-daughter gave birth to but twenty kittens during a period of seven years.

Asexualization. Asexualization operations are performed on both sexes under a general anesthetic, and when competently handled castration is successful in ninety-eight per cent of cases and spaying in ninety-five per cent of cases, recovery from either operation being made in five days. The effect of asexualization is to direct the male's attention to his home, ending his interest in caterwauling, fighting, night excursions and breeding, to relieve the female of the urge to breed and thus to eliminate the problem of kitten disposal, and in some instances to increase the size of the cat, particularly the male when castrated young.

Castration consists of excising the testicles and cutting away one and three-fourths to two inches of the spermatic cord. To prevent secondary hemorrhage the cord sometimes is tied, sometimes twisted, the latter method (torsion) being considered better for older cats. In very young kittens the cord is crushed. The absence of the testicles stimulates the growth of fatty tissue and the abdomen droops after castration.

Spaying consists of the removal of the ovaries and the destruction of the Fallopian tubes. In the young kitten a three-fourths-inch incision is made in the flank between the hip and the last rib, the ovaries drawn out and the Fallopian tubes crushed. In the older cat the incision is made through the median line.

Chapter Seven

DEVELOPMENT OF THE KITTEN

AT BIRTH the senses of the kitten are undeveloped, and the brain, heart, and circulation also undergo considerable modification in the growing animal. The tail is short, the head and trunk long, and the head is heavy and held up with difficulty for several weeks, this being particularly noticeable in the long-haired kitten. As the kitten grows, the head and trunk become relatively shorter while the tail lengthens.

The sense of touch is present soon after birth, and the kitten responds to warmth almost immediately. It can taste and smell by the third day, and hearing is established soon after. The eyes are imperfectly formed during the first eight or ten days or longer, and a bright light during this period may result in blindness. (The mother cat instinctively selects a shaded spot for her nest.) If kittens born with open eyes survive, they are apt to be weaklings. The eyes on opening are blue and change to the adult color at from a little over five weeks to as many months, the time varying with the individual and the breed.

For seven or eight weeks the legs are unsteady, and from earliest infancy a kitten, when stroked, rears its head, whereas a cat rears its tail.

In nursing, the kitten pushes with its front paws alternately on either side of the nipple as though to press out the milk, and many a grown cat pushes at a carpet or woolen shawl or sweater with the same sensuous enjoyment.

The excreta generally are liquid for five or six weeks and are taken care of by the mother.

After the fourth week the kitten may develop rickets if deprived of sunshine, and male kittens are especially delicate. A serious infectious disease from which the female kitten makes a perfect recovery may produce sterility in the male.

The coat of the kitten is shed at about five months.

Kittens that have not been made acquainted early with the human hand and a knowledge that it is friendly suffer seriously if forcibly taken later. The author once saw two kittens about six weeks old die from fright on their first, sudden encounter with children. They had been born in a back yard where the house was closed for the summer, and never had seen a human being until the children came home, chased and captured them. The kittens expired in their arms. Dissection of a sheep dead from fright after having been chased by dogs revealed that the heart had burst, and perhaps this happened also in the case of the kittens.

Wesley Mills's studies show that purring, growling, and stalking occur in a definite order in the development of the kitten; that on the ninth day the little animal turns its ears in the direction of sound; at five weeks it answers to "Puss, Puss," growls at a dog, and catches its own tail, stalking its mother's soon after; at six weeks it is capable of long concentration, and its will power is much stronger than that of a puppy of the same age and is more intelligently expressed than that of any other animal. He found that the kitten has no control over its tail during the blind period, and tires quickly during the first twenty days; and that at fifteen weeks it shows affection for the whole family and pleasure in being with those it loves. According to Perez the character of the kitten is revealed at sixteen days.

Observations made by the author on several batches of kittens show that their development follows no fixed rule with reference to age. Nothing, in fact, is precisely synchronized in the life of the cat.

The following record shows the development of two domestic short-haired kittens:

At 24 hours one kitten, Hermie, hissed at us, but soon learned that the human presence was friendly. This kitten developed slowly in many respects, but could smell on the second day.

At two days Hermie's brother, Caudie, fought for his mammary rights, striking out to right and left with his tiny front paws. On this day Caudie also stood firmly on his little legs while his brothers and sisters were merely tumbling and groping about.

On the 3d day Hermie fought for a nipple.

On the 7th day faint purring was heard distinctly in the kittens while they were nursing.

On the 10th day Caudie's eyes began to open and were open at fourteen days.

On the 11th day incisors could be felt in the jaws of both kittens.

On the 12th day Caudie recognized the human presence.

On the 13th day he licked his own paws.

On the 14th day he showed signs of play and slapped at his mother.

On the 15th day Hermie's eyes began to open and were open at twenty-one days.

On the 17th day the mother began to play with the kittens, grasping them in her front paws and biting them gently, not hard enough to make them squeal.

On the 18th day the kittens played together, biting and pawing.

On the 20th day Hermie arched his back after a nap and on the 21st day Caudie did the same.

On the 21st day Hermie licked his paws with catlike, biting movement, and washed Caudie's face. On this day molars and premolars could be felt in the jaws of both kittens.

At three weeks and three days Caudie began to romp and Hermie made as if to play with his mother's tail. All teeth now were cut.

At three weeks and four days Caudie climbed out of the nest box, 10¼ inches high, and ran toward us at the mere sound of our voice; also cried up from the box at sound of voice.

At three weeks and five days Hermie began to run on the floor and Caudie climbed the table legs, sunk his claws in the carpet, and ran with a pronounced noise on the carpet.

At four weeks and one day Caudie began to pounce and to lap water.

At four weeks and two days he ate boiled peas of his own accord and lapped milk.

At four weeks and five days Hermie folded his front paws under.

At five weeks and one day Hermie's eyes began to show a tinge of green, while Caudie's remained a clear blue.

At six weeks the mother brought them a tiny mole in which they showed no interest.

At seven weeks the mother was given an English sparrow just shot out of doors and, though hungry herself, insisted on taking it in to her babies. Hermie seized it but could do nothing but growl until Caudie was removed, when he proceeded to eat the bird.

At four months and fourteen days one of Hermie's lower cuspids became loose.

Observations made on a batch of half Persian kittens showed quicker development in some respects, slower in others. Their eyes began to open on the third and fourth days, some had both eyes open on the fifth day, and all within a week. Purring, however, was not heard until the ninth day. At two weeks they tried to leave the nest. On the twenty-first day they began to romp and play with one another, though still very wobbly on their legs, also to play with a bit of paper, carrying it in the mouth, and ate Boston beans, washing their faces afterward.

The foregoing observations show that the domestic cat may begin to shed its claws at three weeks and five days, and that it is not ready for raw meat until seven weeks old.

Chapter Eight

LONGEVITY IN CATS

(A Record of Seventeen Cats from Twenty-one to
Thirty-one Years of Age)

THE AVERAGE age of the cat is reckoned as fourteen years, but many reach eighteen or nineteen. Most cats meet with a tragic end, therefore relatively few records of their life span are possible, and an accurate figure has not been arrived at. They are naturally healthy animals and no doubt naturally long-lived. Our slender records of longevity are principally of male and neuter male cats, but it is likely that, as among wild felines, the female is normally slightly longer lived.

Whenever an old cat dies in the United States some veterinarian is asked to give an equivalent in age between the cat and a human being, and sensational guesses have been made for the benefit of an avid press. A cat of twenty-six has been called the equal of a man of one hundred and twenty-five, one of twenty-three the equal of a person of one hundred and forty, a cat of but twenty the equal of a man of one hundred and fifty, and so on. A definite method is needed for arriving at these conclusions. We have the authenticated records of two North American cats of thirty-one years, and in England one said to be authentic and two unauthenticated records have been published of cats of the same age and another of a cat of thirty-three years. Among people, where centenarian societies have existed, the oldest members have been slightly over one hundred and three and a few have reached one hundred and six. It is eminently fair, therefore, to take thirty-one and one hundred and three and one-third respectively as the maximum age of cat and man, and this gives us the following table:*

A cat of	*Is the equivalent of a*
1 year	child of 3 years 4 months
7 years	man of 23 years 4 months
14 years	man of 46 years 4 months
21 years	man of 70 years
28 years	man of 93 years 4 months
31 years	man of 103 years 4 months

At twenty-one years, therefore, a cat may be said to have reached its threescore and ten, and thereafter it lives on borrowed time.

The following data cover seventeen cats that lived for from twenty-one to thirty-one years. These data are from questionnaires sent to the owners of the cats and filled out by them or by a member of the family. Ten of the animals were neuter males, three males, and four females. All but two were short-haired, and all but four died a natural death. These four were destroyed because of helplessness or disease. Four were black; five white with yellow, gray or black markings, or with both gray and black; four were gray and black, Tom Cummins Converse having been a perfect nar-

*The age equivalents for rat and man, formulated by Doctor H. H. Donaldson of Wistar Institute, in which a rat of three years is reckoned as the equivalent of a man of ninety, are based on the rate at which the weight is doubled after birth, and on the average life span of the rat, longevity being eliminated. This method therefore does not apply to aged cats.

Born	Died	Age	Name	Sex	Owned by
1917	1939	21	Tweetie Heart	Female Persian	Dr. Donald T. MacPhail, New York City
1909	1930	21	Kitty	Neuter Persian	Dr. C. G. Rohrer, New York City
1913	1934	21	Nig	Female	Hon. Henry Boyer, Raymond, Wash.
1915	1936	21	Monk Hollinshead	Neuter	Mr. and Mrs. H. W. Hollinshead, Newark, N.J.
1917	1939	22	Beauty	Female	Mrs. Anne Nugent, Hartford, Conn.
1915	1937	22	William	Neuter	Mrs. Alfred Nocka, Richmond, Va.
1909	1932	23	Hex	Neutered at 14	Mrs. Wm. L. Hebblethwaite, Chelsea, Mass.
1913	1936*	23	Old Tom	Neuter	Mr. Charles Huiras, Canby, Oregon
1915	1938	23	Tom Beaver	Neuter	Mr. and Mrs. W. A. Beaver, Bend, Oregon
1915	1939	24	Tommy Clark	Male	Dr. W. L. Clark, Seneca Falls, N.Y.
1910	1934*	24	Sport	Neuter	Mrs. Harold D. Spicer, Paw Paw, Mich.
1914	1938*	24	Tom Cummins Converse	Neuter	Mr. and Mrs. Charles Converse, Oswego, N.Y.
1910	1935*	25	Uncle Sammy	Male	Mr. and Mrs. Wm. M. Hoyt, South Royalton, Vt.
1910	1936	26	Potty Allen	Neuter	Mrs. Wynne Allen, Kansas City, Mo.
1910	1938	28	Goldie	Male	Mr. H. E. Wheaton, Groton, Conn.
1904	1935	31	Tommy Bond	Neuter	Mr. Thomas Bond, Whitewood, Saskatchewan, Canada
1906	1937	31	Mother Cat	Neuter	Mrs. Hamilton Luddy, San Andreas, Calif.

87

*Put to sleep.

row-striped tabby; one was "almost white with brown and gray markings," one was yellow, one silver, and one smoke; *i.e.,* in thirteen of the cats black was present in greater or lesser degree. (In any miscellaneous collection of short-haired domestic cats, about ten out of fifteen will be found to have black in the coat.)

In summarizing the data supplied to us concerning these remarkable felines, we find that *the aging cat remains closer to its home,* though often it will mouse or play to the end unless incapacitated. Goldie never left the house except on a leash, to which he was trained at ten years. Tom Converse, at twenty-four, would go to meet his master and stand up to be carried into the house. Monk Hollinshead loved to be entertained at home, and in his twenty-second year enjoyed a ride about the house in a box lid, or about the kitchen on a large sheet of paper.

The aging cat often grows quieter, sleeps more, talks less and plays less, becomes more affectionate and increasingly dependent on human beings, and also more eager for admiration. Tweetie Heart slept two-thirds of the time. Tom Converse often gazed at himself in a mirror, and would roll over when told. Potty* would do tricks to attract the attention of guests and if noticed would overdo it, as children generally do. When visitors were leaving the house and Mr. and Mrs. Allen accompanied them to the car, Potty walked beside them, and when they turned to re-enter the house he did the same, "as though having said good-by." He feared water and ran indoors when rain began to fall. He loved the smell of flowers. He loved to box with Mrs. Allen. Monk

---

*His original name of Spotty was changed to Potty, which could be pronounced more quickly when calling him.

Hollinshead, after twenty years, was no longer able to leap to the shoulder of his loved master when the latter was seated, but reached up to be lifted to it. On his twenty-first birthday he received a new food dish, assisted in the removal of the wrapper, properly approved the gift, but in keeping with the dignity of his advanced years, refrained from exuberance and sat quietly in the dish, putting all four feet close together and wrapping his tail around. William, as he aged, could not bear to have Mrs. Nocka out of his sight and was called her shadow. He ate at table with her, slept on her bed, went visiting with her, was sad if she was, and would not eat if she were sick. He was an exception in becoming more talkative with age.

Like people, some show their age and some do not. William, at twenty-two, "seemed no older than at eight." Tom Converse, at twenty-four, presented the appearance of a much younger cat. At twenty-one Monk looked very old.

Some never killed birds or mice. William, in his entire life, caught only three mice and these he carried home unhurt. Doctor MacPhail tells us that Tweetie Heart never injured a bird or mouse.

All care for their coats as long as physically able to do so, though the coat sometimes grows shabby with age. In two instances coats which have had no black are described as having become "downy," *i.e.,* Tommy Clark's and William's. Occasionally an old cat, like an old gentleman, becomes dapper and fussily immaculate, at about seventeen years, busying himself much more assiduously with his toilet than when younger.

It appears that the breeding period may continue much longer than heretofore believed, though our meager data do not permit of an exact statement as to when old cats discontinue breeding. We have records of only three males and four females. Our males are Tom Beaver, who bred up to twenty-two, Tom Converse, who bred up to the time of his death at twenty-four, and Potty Allen, who began to stay at home three nights out of four when eighteen years old and after twenty-three courted no more. It is interesting to note that William was neutered when fourteen years old, as he had then begun to spray in the house. Of the four females, Nig, who died at twenty-one, began to breed at one year and had her last maternity at about eighteen and one-half years. Her litters always were small and not too frequent. Beauty began to breed at two years and stopped at sixteen. Her litters were small and she had in all only twenty-eight kittens, but one of which is living. Tweetie Heart began to breed in her second year and had her last litter when seventeen years old. It consisted of but two kittens, though her litters up to her thirteenth year had numbered four to six. She averaged three litters every two years, and had her largest families between the ages of five and ten years. Doctor MacPhail says, "She had easily produced 120 kittens in her lifetime." Mother Cat, who reached the astonishing age of thirty-one, began to breed at about two years, her litters averaged from four to six kittens, but she produced only one kitten at her last maternity in 1934, when twenty-eight years old. Her total progeny numbered "208 kittens at least," says Mrs. Luddy.

The weight generally decreases with age, but Hex began to take on flesh at about sixteen years and his weight became cumbersome. The weights of males and neuters in their prime ran from ten to seventeen pounds. Tom Converse, at twenty-four, weighed only seven pounds, and his previous weight is not known. Beauty, at twenty-one, weighed eight pounds as in her prime, and Mother Cat, at thirty-one, weighed eight pounds. Tweetie Heart, at twenty-one, weighed about four pounds and in her prime weighed about five and one-half.

Some old cats suffer from rheumatism or from weakness or paralysis of the hind quarters and may lose control of their sphincter muscles. Potty Allen, however, who had a stroke and died ten days later, when twenty-six years old, arose from his sick-bed and went to his pan up to a few hours before his death, and Hex, though uncomfortably heavy and partly paralyzed, waited for Mrs. Hebblethwaite to carry him out into the yard. Potty, though a male, was always clean in the house. Sport's legs grew weak and though he had the spirit, he was physically unable to get about well in later years.

Some of these cats were great talkers, others seldom spoke, but communicated their wishes by their actions and their eyes. Goldie, at twenty-eight, insisted on having what he wanted, and if it were not forthcoming promptly, "got louder and louder," says Mr. Wheaton.

Some lived largely in the house, others principally out of doors. Old Tom and Tom Beaver, both of Oregon, never slept in the house, and Old Tom never entered the house. Uncle Sammy, until about twenty-three or twenty-four years old, slept on his master's bed, then a basket was provided for him. In his younger days he accompanied Mr. Hoyt all over the farm, riding with him on the wagon seat. He was a great hunter. Kitty was very dignified and liked to pose at windows. He liked to be covered at night when it was cold, and William would slip in under the bedclothes with his head on the pillow like a person.

The majority disliked children, particularly if there were none in their home, but Tom Beaver developed a fondness for children in his later years. Nig was partial to women. Beauty and Mother Cat preferred men. Kitty was timid, as was also Goldie, toward strangers. William was shy toward men until he knew them. Tweetie Heart always held herself aloof from general intimacy. Old Tom and Monk had strong likes and dislikes for people. Monk ignored those he did not like, and no amount of coaxing ever caused him to change his opinion.

The majority liked music and disliked whistling. Tweetie Heart did not dislike either, nor did Mother Cat. Potty Allen disliked both, and sharp or high notes affected Sport's ears. Kitty responded to a whistle. William liked music, and Mrs. Nocka always called him by whistling "Yankee Doodle." Monk was greatly irritated by whistling before he lost his hearing, and would cry constantly and look right at the whistler as if imploring him to stop. Goldie enjoyed music and often walked up and down on the piano keys. Tom Converse disliked whistling, but did not object to the radio.

Black cats grow rusty as well as gray. At nineteen Monk's jet black coat began to show gray hairs and he was very gray around the mouth and on the paws, while his chest and the inner sides of his legs grew rusty. Beauty began to grow gray at twenty.

The hearing sometimes is lost after nineteen years and the eyesight dimmed after twenty-three, but in no case has age affected the memory except that of Tommy Bond, who also grew very deaf in his last few years. Nig and Monk lost their hearing at nineteen years (Monk then becoming very alert to vibrations), Tweetie Heart began to lose her hearing at nineteen, Old Tom became deaf at twenty-three, Uncle Sammy at twenty-four. Otherwise the hearing remained perfect. Old Tom lost his eyesight at twenty-three, Sport's eyes grew dim at about twenty-three, Tommy Bond's eyes became weak and watery at about thirty, and Mother Cat's eyesight began to fail at thirty. In the others the sight remained good.

Loss of the teeth does not occur at any given age. At twenty-eight Goldie had all his thirty teeth, and at twenty-one Kitty had lost none and Nig's were almost perfect. Beauty, at twenty-one, had nineteen teeth left, having lost eleven when ten years old, from eating bones. William lost all but his four canines at nineteen and lost one of these at twenty-one. (He died from an infected tooth.) Old Tom's teeth were mostly good at twenty-three. The other cats lost either their posterior or anterior teeth, Uncle Sammy was toothless for three or four years before he died at twenty-five, and Tommy Bond, at thirty-one, retained only his four cuspids. Tom Converse, at twenty-four, had but five teeth remaining.

The consumption of water sometimes is greatly increased in the aging cat, others take little or none. From one to two cups of water a day was the intake of Tom Beaver, Potty Allen, Monk Hollinshead, Goldie, William, Nig, Sport, Old Tom, and Tommy Bond. Kitty never drank much water, Mother Cat drank very little, Tommy Clark took it sparingly, Beauty did not like it, Tom Converse took less water in winter.

The taste for milk differs. Tweetie Heart never cared

for milk except when she had kittens, Potty Allen could not retain milk, and Hex disliked it; but Uncle Sammy took half a pint a day, and Beauty took from half a pint to nearly a pint, while Tom Converse drank at least a pint a day.

Some always were light eaters, others heavy eaters, and the intake of food generally remains the same or grows less, Tommy Clark being the only cat here recorded who took more nourishment than in his younger days.

For food, *eight of these old felines liked potatoes*—Kitty, Tommy Clark, Tom Converse, Monk Hollinshead, Uncle Sammy, Tommy Bond, Tweetie Heart, and Beauty. Uncle Sammy ate potato with gravy until a few years before his death, and then was fed liver and potato hash. Beauty knew it immediately if a package were brought into the house containing potato chips. Several were fond of table scraps. Potty Allen had his meat raw—liver, kidney, jack rabbit, etc. Hex had his beef cut as for a stew and very well cooked, with a little salt. Much salmon poisoned him. Kitty liked to clean a chop bone, ate meat including ham, also fish and fowl, vegetables including peas, beans, and mashed potatoes, boiled eggs, and Limburger cheese. He was fed regularly but refused to eat regularly, taking his food when he chose. Tommy Clark had a meat diet in winter, including liver, and also ate fish. He ate potatoes and other starchy vegetables sparingly, with chicken or beef gravy. William ate meats, chicken, and vegetables, and liked soups. He received three meals a day and as he aged was given a raw egg beaten in milk on alternate days, and his beef was reduced to half the amount and a teaspoon of liquid peptonoids substituted, with six drops a day of cod liver oil. Goldie ate salmon and other fish. Tom Beaver took milk and meat and latterly brought home his catch which he asked his master to prepare for him. Monk was given no raw meat, but cooked meats, his preference being for lamb, liver, and chicken. He liked also fish, clams, and oysters, and vegetables such as corn, potatoes, asparagus, and mushrooms; also soups, spaghetti, noodles, and cake without icing; and he often received a large dish of warm milk at night. If the family went away for the day his food was left for him, but often he tasted nothing until their return, when he immediately cleaned up the dishes. Beauty's food consisted of corn flakes and shredded wheat with considerable milk for breakfast, vegetables and a little meat with gravy for lunch and dinner. She liked cucumber and cantaloupe, and her vegetables included peas, beans, and potatoes. Mother Cat ate canned fish and fresh liver, and drank much fresh milk. Tom Converse had corn flakes and milk for breakfast, ate potatoes, meat and vegetables (including corn, peas, and carrots), and fish of all kinds, but would take only one helping of cat or dog food.

A few of these cats had traveled, and nearly all had received press notices. Kitty was born in London and was given to Doctor Rohrer when six months old. William was born in Cincinnati and moved with the family a number of times. His twenty-second birthday party was featured in the press, his guests being other pets of the household—cats, dogs, and domestic fowl. Potty Allen lived in Texas until twenty-four years old, when he moved with his owner to Kansas City, and at twenty-six was exhibited at a cat show, taking a blue ribbon for old age. Monk Hollinshead changed homes with his owners, moving from Newark to New Haven, and, a few years later, back to Newark; and he spent many summers with the family at Ocean Grove, New Jersey. Tommy Clark, when a tiny kitten, was found by Doctor Clark on a wintry night in February, 1915, in a manger. He was given wide publicity, received 1239 pieces of mail on the occasion of his twenty-fourth birthday, and 300 human guests attended his birthday banquet. Hex came to Mrs. Hebblethwaite when about three months old. He had been terribly abused and starved, and about two inches of his tail were gone. For a year or more, whenever he heard a strange man's step he crouched close to the ground and quickly secreted himself.

Cats belonging to veterinarians enjoy visiting the wards. Kitty liked to spend some time in the cat ward, and would play with puppies. Tommy Clark enjoyed horses, and in his younger days slept in the box stalls. When a horse was suspended in slings he rubbed around its legs as though helping to keep away the flies by day, and slept in a hay manger at night. He was fond of water, running under the spray from the hose in summer, also taking a bath by jumping into a pail of water and out again. He performed a number of tricks including shaking hands.

Beauty, at twenty-one, still stood on her hind legs to be petted and caught a paper ball with her front paws at the count of three. She still cuffed her six-year-old daughter, Juny, if the latter played with things belonging to Beauty. She could still stun a rat, but due to the loss of her front teeth could not kill it. She was contented when riding in an automobile, but it was necessary to cover her head when she entered and left the car.

Some of these cats never were ill, others had severe sicknesses.

In only two instances has it been possible for the owners of the aged cats here described to provide data on the life span of the cat's parents or other forebears, and it therefore *cannot be stated whether longevity is hereditary in cats.* The mother of Beauty, Snukey by name, was brought from Russia when four years old and lived only three years longer. There is no record of the father's age at death. William's father was destroyed when about five years old and his mother died at about the same age. Unfortunately no pedigreed cat whose genealogy has been kept for generations has as yet attained longevity.

REASONS ASSIGNED FOR LONGEVITY

The reason assigned in nearly every case for the great age reached by these ancient felines is "Good care and love," though Doctor Rohrer says he does not know the reason, and Mrs. Converse says "Just lucky and healthy." Some additional reasons are given: Tom Beaver was always fed three times a day; Tweetie Heart never associated with other cats where sickness might be contracted, and she had a fine quality of cleanliness and a happy disposition; Old Tom never had been handled; Tommy Clark "led an easy life and had the personal attention of a veterinarian" (his master). Many cats, however, are clean and happy, receive excellent care, much love and veterinary attention, but die young, and why any animal reaches an age so far in advance of the average for its species is not known.*

From the foregoing data it will be seen that in the cat longevity does not depend upon drinking water, limiting

*Tweetie Heart succumbed to a heart attack (her second) and Tommy Clark died from cancer caused by a dog bite.

the meals to the commonly prescribed two a day, or abstaining from the foods many veterinarians and cat breeders strongly inveigh against—starches, particularly potatoes, rodents, canned salmon, cooked meat. A doctor says of old people, "They get in the habit of living." But what is the reason for this habit? The cause for longevity may lie in some undiscovered chemical harmony of all the cells of the body, whose continued existence revolves about an unconscious principle of "United we stand, divided we fall"; a biological left-over, perhaps, from the days of the early colonial groups in which such an organic solidarity spelled the nearest approach to the potential immortality of the ancestral protozoan. The solution of this perplexing problem is another of the burdens laid upon the biological chemists of the future.

TWO THIRTY-ONE-YEAR-OLD CATS

Tommy Bond and Mother Cat, who reached thirty-one years, are the oldest cats authentically recorded in North America, and as such deserve special mention.

Tommy Bond's age is definitely known because he was born in the same year with a son in the house of his birth and with a daughter in the house of Mr. Bond, where he went to live when twelve years old. Tommy was a great hunter and caught many gophers and rabbits which he carried home to display. On one occasion he took nine gophers in one day, and on another captured and ate two mice at once, the tails of both protruding from his mouth. He had been taught many tricks, such as jumping a loop and standing on his hind feet to drink milk from a cup. He liked children and wanted them to play with him. He

A critical, discriminating cat is Mauja, blue, long-haired, and owned by Mr. and Mrs. J. L. Cilley of Hickory, N. C. She disapproves of Bach.

OLD CATS GROW GRAY AND SHRINK IN WEIGHT

Top: Monk, shown on his twenty-first birthday (Feb. 25, 1936), was gray on head and paws. Courtesy Miss Mildred S. Hollinshead. *Bottom:* Tommy Bond, shown here at thirty, had lost teeth and weight and was losing his sight. Courtesy Mr. Thomas Bond.

loved music but disliked whistling. Often when the radio was playing the old cat sat on a chair with his paws on the radio table, listening intently. He did a great deal of talking up to the last, when his sounds became pitiful, as though he were in distress and trying hard to tell the family what was the matter. He talked more in the early morning when he first entered the house, going upstairs to each bed and mewing loudly until he received an answer. Whenever the family left the house he acted as if he wanted to go too, and was waiting to greet them on their return. Like all the other ancient cats here detailed, he received good care and was greatly loved by all the family. He had a taste for sweet things, and when his appetite failed toward the last, catnip restored it in part. His chief foods were milk, potatoes, and chopped meat, and he drank about two cups of water a day. He was a neuter and in his prime weighed fourteen pounds and measured thirty inches in length. In later years he shrank to eight pounds, grew shabby, and suffered from rheumatism, particularly in his hind quarters. He lost control of his sphincter muscles latterly and was kept outside. His memory was affected in some ways but he always knew and talked to the members of the family, though he was very deaf during his last few years. He could see to the end, but for about a year before his death his eyes were weak and watery. All his teeth had gone save the four cuspids. His colors were white, gray, and black, with a black stripe from the forehead to the tip of the tail. His eyes were gray. He died from old age.

Mother Cat was born April 14, 1906, bred over a period of twenty-six years, producing over two hundred kittens in that time, never was sick, but as to mousing, her owner says,

"She couldn't be bothered." She was somewhat indifferent to people, but favored men. Her foods were canned fish, fresh liver, and much fresh milk. She drank very little water. Her weight was about eight pounds and she took good care of her coat. She performed no tricks, but purred happily when picked up and petted. She did not dislike music or whistling. In the summer of 1932, when she was twenty-six years old, she was taken to the family camp in an automobile, sixty miles from home. Ten days later she disappeared. Three weeks and two days later she reached home. She had not taken the highway, as Mrs. Luddy says she would have been seen in that case, and it is believed that she walked across the country. She looked well and strong and the cushions of her paws "were in remarkably good condition considering her hike," says Mrs. Luddy, who believes her discontent was caused by having no other cats for company. After that summer she went to the camp every year and remained, other cats being present. Her last kitten (neutered) was her companion and playmate from the time of his birth in 1934, when she was twenty-eight years old, to the time of her death in 1937. Her hearing was very good to the last, but her eyesight began to fail at thirty years. She was striped gray and black. Her death was caused by accidental poisoning.

Chapter Nine

THE VOICE AND LANGUAGE
OF THE CAT

VARIOUS FORMS OF EXPRESSION

"CATS," said St. George Mivart, "have a language of their own. Their emotions are expressed by external signs made up of sounds and gestures."

The cat has a very wide range of expression, revealing its emotions not only by means of its voice and its purr, but with its nose, eyes, lips, tongue, ears, paws, tail, back, and fur; in short, with its whole body. The ears are moved in the direction of sound, thrown back in anger or disapproval, and turned forward in joy. The eyes are more expressive of the emotions than those of any other animal save man, and as in many other animals are bright in health and happiness and grow dull under sickness and neglect.

The front paws are used like hands, to grasp a companion or a kitten; to motion for food and attention; to chastise its offspring and other cats, also dogs; to hug a person it loves or pat his cheek; to clasp one's hand when it is about to die. (See other uses, chapters on Physiology and Psychology.)

The tail has an extensive language of its own and the manner in which it is carried is indicative of the cat's state of mind. It twitches with amusement, quakes with excitement, lashes with fury, waves gently with pleasure, is held erect when the world seems gay and a good meal is in prospect, is lowered in fright, is fluffed up with fur on end when the animal is startled, and otherwise used to express many emotions.

The lips smirk, smile, and kiss the object of the animal's affection—another cat, or a person. Mrs. Alfred Nocka writes us:

Before eating, William [described in the chapter on Longevity] always kissed my cheek until his last year, when he would get on my lap and kiss me six or seven times right on the mouth. Sometimes he would be dreaming and suddenly jump up and run to me and start kissing and talking to me as though he had dreamed that I had given him away or he had gotten lost.

The nose, though small, can be puckered with anxiety, uplifted to catch an interesting odor, or laid lovingly against the cheek of a friend. The tongue gives an affectionate lick to the hand of a loved person, while the head is pressed against his neck. One Pennsylvania cat thrusts his tongue out repeatedly when greatly pleased with a tidbit. The teeth are used to give a gentle bite of affection or remonstrance. The back is arched in fear and the fur of the back, as well as that of the tail, bristles with apprehension. By rearing its back while the hair is standing on end, the cat makes itself look larger to an enemy.

THE VOICE

With its voice the cat not only expresses its casual emotions in various mews, but by hissing (called swearing), spitting, growling, screeching, and caterwauling.

The language of the cat is varied and it is little understood, partly because several different sounds may be used to convey the same meaning. Marvin R. Clark (reputed to have been blind) professed to have discovered that it is made up of one hundred words, a list of which he published. His work is a curious mixture of sense and nonsense. Nearly all students of the voice of the cat and dog have observed that though the dog uses only consonants, the cat uses also vowels, but there is some disagreement as to what are the cat's consonants.

Clark named them as b, d, f, l, m, p, r, t, v, w, and y. Dupont de Nemours, eighteenth-century naturalist, Chateaubriand, and others agreed upon f, g, h, m, n, and v. Carl Van Vechten* stresses p, r, s, t, and says he never heard a cat say v. Pollock doubted that cats ever use h or v. In the various cat sounds given by Beachcroft one may find c, h, k, m, p, q, r, s, t, v, w, and x.†

Studies made by the author show that the cat uses ch, f, h, k, l, m, n, p, r, s, t, w, and the semivowel y.

The fighting sounds are comprised chiefly of h, w, and y, as *ah, aah, ooh, waa, wah, wow, yah.* In hunger sounds h, m, r, and w predominate, as *mrr-aow, mwaa-owoo, wah-oo-aw, ooh-aah-oo-oo.* The sexes in calling each other use m, p, and r, as *prr-rah-oo, prr-mao-oo, prr-roo;* and a male calling a friend used h, k, and m, as *mak-mah-oo.* A kitten says *fitl!* and *chik!* and in hissing, *haah!* A cat in spitting uses a prolonged sibilant—*fitsss!* also, in hissing, *haah!* A female cat, shrieking at her mate, uses h and m, as *mah-aa-ah-ah-oo-oo.* After the breeding season the male uses principally h, m, and w, and occasionally p and r, as *wah-oo, ma-owh, maa-aow, prr-mah-oo* (*a* as in mat). A male sauntering along and wishing for something to turn up, either a bite or a fight, uses h, m, w, and y, as *yah-oo, mee-ow-oo,*

---

*"The Cat in Music," *Musical Quarterly,* Oct., 1920, p. 573.
†*Just Cats,* by Luard and Beachcroft, 1936.

or *wow-wow-oo*. Many cats say *now* when wishing to go out. This is distinct from *meow* as said at other times. On one occasion, in the evening, the author heard a cat say distinctly several times, *ark-oo-murry,* with the inflection on the last syllable. Though we have listened for two years for a repetition of this sound in the hope of ascertaining whether it was uttered by a male cat and for what reason, it never has been repeated.

The English cat mews, the Indian cat myaus, the Chinese cat says mio, the Arab cat naoua, and the Egyptian cat mau; and to illustrate how difficult it is to interpret the cat's language, her mew is spelled in thirty-one different ways, five examples being maeow, me-ow,* mieaou, mouw, and murr-raow! Perhaps we are to be excused when it is considered that some cats have a different mew for every occasion.

The voice of the domestic cat commonly covers two full octaves in ascent from the middle *c*. Most often it is pitched on the *c* above the middle *c* and the notes just below and above this—*b, c* sharp, and *d,* with half tones also, the most extensive range of voice being exercised by the fighting tom, who may embrace a complete octave in one yell, ascending from *g* sharp above the middle *c* to *c, d* sharp, and *g* sharp, with a screech on the upper *g* sharp and a concluding growl on the lower. Or two males, when chorusing, may strike notes exactly one octave apart, and the voice of one simulates a toy balloon from which the air is slowly escaping, while that of the other bubbles as though he had something hot in his mouth or were blowing bubbles in his throat; and his small red tongue moves in and out, licking his chops as though in pleasant anticipation of tast-

*"There's the sea puss. Just hear her me-ow!"—Kate Upson Clark.

ing his adversary's blood. Their octave does not long harmonize in the duet, for a switch is made to another key, the harmonious *g's* being abandoned for a *wah-wah-woo* on the *b* above the middle *c*, the *d* above that, and the *b* again. The *g* and *g* sharp above the middle *c* are notes also of distress in a tom who believes he is deserted or cries for attention. The female, when hungry, uses these *g's* also. When in heat she calls on two notes, the *a* and *c* above the middle *c*. A feverish *prr* is uttered on the *a, rah,* or *mah* on the *c* above, and *oo* on the *a* again. In coitus she screams on the second *g* above the middle *c*. The hungry male more often calls on *b, c,* and *c* sharp above the middle *c*, though he may change instantly and loudly to the *g* and *b* flat above, then resume his plaint on the *b* and *c's,* in normal tones.

The cat does not always begin and end by uttering only two or three notes. The principal notes may be *g* above the middle *c* and the *c* above that, but the cry may begin on *f* below the *g*, touch *f* sharp, then the *g*, which is emphasized, and every note may be sounded and slurred, including some half notes, in the ascent from the *g* to the *c* above, which also is emphasized. There may then be a drop to the *a* below this *c* for the final, softer note.

The caterwauling of the cat is definitely feral. Bailey's *English Dictionary* of 1755 defines it thus: "Catter-wawl (from Gutterwaul, to cry among Gutters), to cry as Cats do when they are proud." A gutter he defines as "a Canal or Rain-spout for Water," indicating that it was situated on the roof; and proud, he says, means "elated or puffed up in Mind."

Both sexes are subject to this "elation," and a female gives her head the same semicircular twist that characterizes a male when challenging a rival; and she chastises a female cat in the same manner in which he chastises his rival. She caterwauls with an equally raucous voice.

It has been suggested that were one to hear these sounds for the first time resounding on the quiet country air, one certainly would conclude that they were made by a wild animal. The sounds of dogs fighting to the death do not trouble the human ear, but the cries of cats in a battle from which both will emerge only a little scratched or ear-bitten drive many people frantic with the desire to throw water or missiles to end the combat. This impulse is speedily checked by an endeavor intelligently to understand the delicate nuances of cat music. Then it changes instantly from the irritating to the intriguing, as we begin to realize that our aversion has been due not solely to the fact that the sounds are feral, nor yet to the fact that cats are feminine animals and therefore not expected to fight, but to our failure to comprehend the high-pitched voices, the vowels and half tones, and the great variety of cat language. A definite soprano and contralto combine in a duet whose "overtones" fall harshly on the human ear, which suffers no disturbance from a dog's monotonous consonants, and only by recording them on a phonograph could we learn the tune of each.*

Nor are these duets always combative. Spotty, for example, spies Blackie, a newcomer in the neighborhood, and begins a duet while careering sidewise toward Blackie, head twisted, one shoulder askew, like a kitten at play. Blackie may approach cautiously to touch noses, or he may settle

---

*The sounds of quarreling cats have inspired numerous song writers. In Switzerland the beer gardens commonly provide an amusing cat song as an alternative to serious yodeling, rendered, like the yodel, by a man and a woman. It is interspersed with loud and threatening "oo-wah-oo's" and ends with mutual spitting and clawing.

where he is and, comfortably folding his front paws under him, take up his part of the moaning refrain as casually as a woman knitting and singing in a rocking-chair, and without so much as glancing at Spotty. As in most cat duets the male that begins uses soprano, while the answering male starts approximately one octave lower, but in this case the former descends while the latter ascends. To human ears the sounds are disharmonious, but the duet proceeds without violence. The prancing Spotty comes to a halt within two feet of Blackie, then quietly walks away or climbs a fence. Up to this point it has been a neighborly greeting, but it proceeds no further in this pacific groove. The next time they meet there may be a clash.

A tom cat is particularly resentful upon discovering a rival perched a foot or so above him, and fierce and high is his scream of rage and defiance.

The sounds in which an animal is interested and the tones it can differentiate appear to depend in large part upon the extent of the vocal utterances of its species, since cats hear many sounds and distinguish many tones to which dogs and other animals with a more limited range of voice are deaf.* A cat uses and is particularly susceptible to the sounds of sibilants, readily responding to the call, "ss-ws-ss."

The tone inflections of the cat's voice cover a considerable range of meaning. By the use of tones and half tones it says many things: that it is curious, eager, fond of one, impatient, offended, angry, hungry, satisfied, grateful, jealous, and much else; or it asks a question.

*If a herd of cows browsing in a field is facing in one direction and a person stands 200 feet behind it and imitates a calf, the entire herd will face about, but will not do this if unfamiliar sounds are employed.

Swinburne, *en rapport* with his cat, said,

> Just your foot upon my hand
> Softly bids it understand.

But he does not say how much he really did understand. The cat has so much to say that even its range of sounds is entirely inadequate, and its futile efforts to make us comprehend it often are grievous.*

Reverend John G. Wood, the naturalist, says that his cat, Pret, when looking out of a window, ordinarily could see only three things—a bird, another cat, or a human being, and when asked what he was looking at answered in a different manner according to which it was. If a bird he chattered; if a cat he mewed and rocked himself as if making ready for a spring; if a man he gave a long, thin mew and looked around to be sure Mr. Wood was at hand in case of invasion. But one day when he saw a dog he could not answer, not having any word for "dog."

The trembling, soft call of the mother cat to her young, which Lafcadio Hearn styled "a soft, trilling coo, a pure caress of tone," is seldom used at any other time, and a mother cat, having lost her only kitten, talked to it in just this manner, though knowing it was dead. On one occasion we heard a tom cat use the same call to a female friend who was ill.

When offended or deserted a male cat sometimes cries in loud protest for several days.

Some cats talk a great deal, and Mrs. Edith W. Berwyn informs us that her shaded silver, Raudee, not only replied when spoken to (many cats do this), but talked to himself when he could not get what he wanted.

*". . . so touching in their dumbness."—John Galsworthy.

UNDERSTANDING OF OUR LANGUAGE

We speak to the cat in English and usually it understands. It is sensitive to the purport of the different intonations of the human voice and in fact may grasp what we wish to convey though no word is spoken.

It is said that Gottfried Mind, "The Raphael of Cats," carried on a sort of conversation with his favorite cat, Minette, by means of gestures and words. Within certain limits the cat knows what is said to it and also about it, and takes what is said very seriously. When quite young it learns the meaning of some simple words such as in, out, water, milk, meat, fish, bed, bird, ball, button, collar.

Sarah E. Trueblood tells of a cat named Ginger who knew the words corn, crab, and kidney, and on hearing any of them would jump on the shoulders of the person who suggested that he have some. We are not told that he knew anything more than that each word meant something to eat. His mother knew the name of her medicine and would leave the room abruptly if she heard it and saw anyone going to the medicine cabinet.* Mrs. Edith W. Berwyn's cats, when asked if they "want some eats," all lick their chops.

Mrs. Alfred Nocka's cat, William (described in chapter on Longevity), when young met with an accident in which he lost the first claw of one of his fore feet and eventually a large ugly nail grew in its place. The family called it "William's great toe." When asked where his great toe was, William always showed it and "talked about it."

Mrs. Nocka sends us the following anecdote:

Some years ago two starlings were having a dreadful battle in

Cats by the Way, 1904.

the yard. They made so much noise that without giving a thought to what I was saying I called William and said, "Will you please make those birds stop fighting?" I was shocked when I saw him running out, for fear he might hurt them, but he walked up to them, batted them with his paw and sent them as far as he could, then came into the house with a sort of "I-fixed-them-both" look. It was months before I could realize that he must have understood just what I wanted.

When Mrs. William G. Rogers of Yonkers, New York, discovered that her twelve-year-old cat, Boots, had nine rugæ, she told him he ought to be a good hunter but that she never had known him to catch a bird. He went out and later returned with a sparrow, to which he called her attention with a profusion of speech. Sometimes cats learn the names of the different members of the household and have been known to fetch one of the family when instructed to do so. When told to wake up the children they will run up-stairs, jump on the bed and purr, and sometimes pat gently on a child's body to rouse it.

Miss Saranac, a cat belonging to Miss Agnette Terner of Saranac Lake, New York, has a favorite cloth button which she retrieves, and if told to get her button goes to the drawer where it is kept. When asked if she would like to go for a car ride, she fetches her collar.

THE PURR OR SONG

The purr of the cat has been called "humming speech," in that it appears to correspond with the low, contralto humming of a human being. It is part of the cat's language, and spreads contentment on the atmosphere.

Purring or singing notes are pitched much lower than

the voice, commonly below instead of above the middle *c*. A very young cat purrs in a monotone, sometimes inhaling softly and exhaling loudly, often on *b* flat or *g* sharp below the middle *c;* but grown cats of both sexes purr on two notes, such as *c* and *e,* or *f* and *a,* below the middle *c.* These notes, as indicated, generally are separated by only one note. Sometimes they are interlarded with a slurring of several notes as though a tune were being attempted. Some cats with very little voice can purr loudly, and one of the author's Angoras who was afflicted with bronchitis in winter and also after snake-hunting in a swamp, lost her voice at such times but not her purr, which was exceedingly loud. In some cases the purr, though inaudible, can be felt by placing the fingers on the ribs of the animal.

THE GROWL

A cat's growls sound alike to the human ear but have different meanings which a kitten instantly understands though it never heard them before. The warning growl of a mother cat when she sees a dog or a tom cat means "Fade away," and causes the kittens, her own and others, to rush for shelter. Her warning growl when she wishes to wean the kittens means "Steer clear or I'll slap you," and causes them to step quickly aside. Another growl is that given by a cat with a bone or other morsel which it does not intend to share. A kitten knows that this growl will be followed by a scratch and remains at a safe distance, though eagerly eyeing and keenly desiring the tidbit.

There are several kinds of growls besides these—pugnacious, angry, remonstrative, the growl of pain, and others.

Chapter Ten

THE CAT'S EAR FOR MUSIC

THE CAT loves, hates, or is indifferent to music. Some cats favor the piano, some the organ, others prefer the harp or the violin; and many love to be sung to sleep and indicate a desire for more if the singing ceases. Jenny Lind's name might never have been known except that her pet cat loved music and the nine-year-old girl sang to it in a window, thereby attracting the attention of a passer-by who happened to recognize her musical gift. Her education for twenty years at the expense of the Swedish Government followed.* We have no record of the cat's response to the accordion, an instrument which one cat lover believes most nearly harmonizes with its own musical tones. We can imagine that the soft Hindu flute would appeal to cats, and no doubt their oriental ears are better adapted than ours to catch its subtle intricacies. Since it is only during relatively recent centuries that they have heard occidental music, perhaps all cats have not yet become accustomed to it. With a radio in the house the suffering of music-hating cats must be intense. The music lovers, however, approach the radio when there is music, even lying upon it as if they could not be too close to the source of their pleasure. Most cats like instru-

* "The Jenny Lind Centennial Celebration," by Ida M. Mellen, *Bulletin,* New York Zoological Society, November, 1920, p. 130.

ments with a few strings, also gentle bells, and doubtless the cats of old enjoyed the simple sounds of the Egyptian sistrum—a musical rattle used in the worship of Isis and composed of a thin oval metal band (one in the British Museum is of copper) fastened to a handle and crossed by movable metal rods or rods bearing rings. Sarah B. Wister found that two cords tied to a transverse rod with little bells at the end make a gymnastic and musical device for cats. One would spring from the ground and seize a cord in each paw, swinging herself to and fro while the bells jingled. It is possible that the sacred cats of Egypt played with the sistrum in like manner.

Deaf people enjoy musical vibrations when they cannot hear melodies, and deaf cats also enjoy the vibrations caused by piano and violin playing. Though an occasional cat favors the sound of whistling and can even be summoned by a whistle, many cats, like many people, are keenly disturbed by it. If a cat's ear is sensitive it will exhibit restlessness and inability to sleep while obnoxious whistling is in progress and may attempt to stop it. There are many instances in which cats have put their paws against the lips of a whistler.

Some cats hate almost every form of human music, others are not only fond of instrumental or vocal music, but show a partiality for certain tunes and a disapproval of others.

Mrs. W. Chance relates an amusing case in which the master of the house drove one of their cats literally to desperation by whistling a tune which was greatly disliked (the tune, apparently, and not the whistle, was the object of the cat's aversion), and "when she could no longer stand the excruciating noise, she suddenly ran up him like a squirrel up a pine tree and delicately bit his nose."*

Miss Lucretia Wilson of New York City owned a cat named Jack who hated radio music and removed himself as far as possible from it—unless there were crooning, in which case he approached and listened intently.

In the home of Mr. and Mrs. J. L. Cilley of Hickory, North Carolina, their young daughter sits at the piano of an evening to practise her lessons and entertain her parents with pieces she has learned. Mauja, a long-haired blue cat, remains unconcerned until the child begins to play a certain selection of Bach's, then, looking bored, invariably goes to the piano and sits on the bench beside her until the selection is finished, after which she leaves and turns an indifferent ear to the remainder of the program. Of course the cat hates Bach, otherwise she would look pleased. Were the girl to sing Bach, the animal would no doubt close her mouth with her paw, but she does not know how to stop the piano. We learn that the selection to which the cat objects is the Two-Part Invention Number 13. This is a smooth, simple exercise, but one in which even the dull human ear may detect a faint resemblance to that unmelodious rising and falling crescendo typical of caterwauling, though it takes a cat to call one's attention to it. She disapproves of it because cats have a natural prejudice against imitations. We have not ascertained whether Bach disliked cats, but perhaps this would make little difference, for cats may enjoy Meyerbeer, who hated felines, or even Brahms, who, according to Wagner, was viciously cruel to them.

That a cat discerns very fine differences of sound is illus-

*A Book of Cats, 1898.

trated by the fact that it instantly knows the difference
between the call of the female and the cry of the male, and
between her screech and his. Few human beings, even after
some study, are able to distinguish between these sounds.

Since the ear of the cat is so analytical it is not surprising
that some musicians have credited their successes to the
criticisms of an attentive feline. It is certain that when cats
are sensitive to music they cannot endure poor singing or
shrill notes, and professional singers, as well as amateurs,
practising in the home, have been interrupted when they
struck a harsh note by having a protesting paw placed
against their mouths. This action commonly is misinter-
preted as a desire to get at the sound.

Cats are affected also by noises of different degrees of
intensity, and greatly appreciate being directed to some se-
cluded spot during Fourth of July celebrations.

A cat's fine recognition of tone is illustrated by the fact
that it can be taught to come into a room to be fed when
a certain note is sounded and will remain where it is
when another note is struck. Miss Lucy G. Wolfe of Scran-
ton, Pennsylvania, tells us that the method of disciplining
Spunky, her smoke Persian, is for one of the family to step
to the piano and strike the first *c* below the middle *c*. This
is all that is needed. "If he is doing something he shouldn't,
he stops and leaves hurriedly for the cellar." She says the *c*
has not been used on him in months.

Some cats like to twang the strings of a guitar and almost
all cats enjoy walking on the keys of a piano. A kitten that
developed a habit of sleeping on top of the piano fell onto
the keys one day and was so delighted with the sounds
produced that he spent much time then and thereafter

walking up and down the keyboard. It is well known that the *Cat's Fugue* by the younger Scarlatti interprets in part the sounds made by a cat walking up the keyboard of a piano and that Chopin's *Valse Brillante* was inspired by the notes struck by his cat when padding over the keys.

Cats amuse themselves by ringing bells (accomplished by the pulling of a rope or pushing of a button) and they like to walk on the clicking keys of a typewriter. The rhythmic ticking of a clock is pleasing to them, and some enjoy stopping and starting a hall clock by striking the pendulum. No doubt the motion of the pendulum in this case is as fascinating to the eye as is the tick to the ear.

The cat's own ability to "sing" is treated in the foregoing chapter.

Chapter Eleven

THE PSYCHOLOGY OF THE CAT

GENERAL INTELLIGENCE

THE VERDICT of scientists who have studied the cat is that it is a large-brained, perfect mammalian.

W. H. Hudson, the great naturalist who devoted considerable attention to a study of the mind of this animal, said, "Cats are mentally very near to us; their brains function even as ours do, far as we have risen above them in all mental powers." He thought their powers of reflection could not be easily distinguished from what we call reflection in ourselves.

No competent observer doubts that the cat thinks. As defined by the *Standard Dictionary,* thought is "the act, process or power of thinking," and this applies to both worded and unworded thoughts. Despite the fact that the cat has an extensive language of its own, the thought without words may be the kind it exercises, a simple and effective way of thinking which strongly resembles instinct in its rapid results. When we talk of "thinking quickly," we most often mean we are thinking without words. We can only guess that the cat may do this. St. George Mivart, another great naturalist who studied the psychology of the cat, said, "We cannot, of course, without becoming cats, perfectly understand the cat mind."

In the matter of brains, cats, like people, exhibit varying degrees of intelligence in the long range from morons to geniuses. Like people also they sometimes lose their minds, and sometimes are born insane.

The different species of large cats differ radically in brain structure, and individuals among them vary as much as do individuals among domestic cats. The latter, however, are strongly influenced by the amount of attention paid to them. Reverend John G. Wood remarked, "The cat displays an intellectual power which would be equalled by very few dogs and surpassed by none." This is particularly applicable when cats are made members of a family and talked to a great deal. In the words of Miss Edna M. Hopkins of Carbondale, Pennsylvania, "They bloom under the impetus of love."

Dupont de Nemours made some studies of the domestic cat and concluded that its ability to climb trees furnishes it with resources of experience and ideas denied the dog, but we have no knowledge that the big cats that do not climb trees are less resourceful and intelligent than other members of the cat tribe, which are in general notable examples of efficiency and persistence.

Charles Dudley Warner's cat, Calvin, would select a spot in the garden from which the view was best, and sit there for hours contemplating the scenery. "His habits of observation," said Warner, "have given him a trained mind and made him philosophical."

Champfleury, a great cat lover, said, "If you would know what the cat is thinking about, you must hold its paw in your hand for a long time." This is just another way of saying that you must try to understand the animal. Before attempting to become *en rapport* with it, however, as has been said before, it is well to remember that though the dog never sees through you, the cat does.

A cat cannot understand punishment unless it proceeds as a direct result of the act itself. If it catches a bird and is whipped, it will catch more birds. If it catches a bird and the bird is made to peck its nose, it will never touch another.

Cats, as a rule, do not seem to understand that human beings cannot see in near darkness, but a bobtail cat, Jumper, knows that one member of the family is blind. His owner, Mrs. Roy A. Lee of Waymart, Pennsylvania, says, "My brother is blind and always sits at the end of the porch. When the cat wishes to come in, if any one else is on the porch he walks to the door; but if my brother is there alone, he walks across the porch and tells him he would like to come in by jumping on him."

Among wild felines it appears that the females are more alert and resourceful than the males, since they must not only provide their own food and evade enemies, but care for, feed and protect the young; but there is no proof that in the long-domesticated cat one sex is more intelligent than the other. The many authenticated records in this book show equal resourcefulness and intelligence in both sexes.

Lovey de Joy, a mother cat owned by the author in childhood, had many an English sparrow brought down from a back-yard cherry tree with a Flobert rifle in the hands of an older brother, Fred. When the gun was brought out she would pet the holder, and at the sound of the discharge (it was almost noiseless, the ammunition consisting of a mere trace of fulminite of mercury) she rushed to the door to be let out, and if she did not find the bird in our yard, sought it in a neighboring yard, sometimes clearing the fence without touching it in her eagerness for her breakfast. This fence was five and one-half feet high.

Miss Lucy G. Wolfe tells us that when her father and mother were ill at the same time and the nurse did not come on duty until eight o'clock, she went down-stairs to get breakfast first. "One morning," she says, "I heard Mother awake, left my breakfast on the table and took her coffee and toast up to her. When I returned my bacon was gone but on my plate was Spunky's catnip mouse."

Pierre Loti said of his cat, La Moumouette, "As soon as she sees that knife and fork and spoon are lying at her plate, she assumes that she is not accepted at table and retires without umbrage to the piano stool, which is her refuge on such occasions. Those who deny that animals are capable of reasoning may explain this conduct as best they can."

Harrison Weir tells of a cat whose kitten had wandered off and who took the kitten's plaything, a rabbit leg, and lured him home with it. He also tells of a cat who, seeing a large rat, grabbed her kitten and jumped up to a high drawer in which she deposited it before attacking the rat. She killed the rat and took it to her mistress, then returned and took the kitten out of the drawer.

Mr. Walter L. Hamilton of Holyoke, Massachusetts, while doing some electrical engineering at the Parsons Paper Company's mill in his town, took the black mill cat, Betsy Parsons, a small bottle of milk every day. One day he forgot it and tried to evade the cat by taking an underground passage, but she had spied him, and going around another way, met him in the middle of the passage. (He never forgot the milk again.)

Hudson tells of a cat that stalked birds every day on the

lawn after his mistress threw out crumbs for them, but never caught any. One day the cat went and sat in the middle of the becrumbed area for an hour, waiting for the birds to come down, but they did not appear. He tried this for three days and on the fourth day discontinued stalking the birds and never took any further interest in them. He had reasoned that they wouldn't come down if they saw him approaching, therefore he would be there in advance. This also failing to work, he desisted altogether.

Mivart thought the domestic cat's adaptation of means to ends truly remarkable, and he observed that it draws practical inferences. Two instances have been sent us in which the owners thought the cat might have learned a hard lesson by inference. One relates to a New Zealand tom cat who "was very timid and frightened of men, and because of his timidity was always quarreling with the other cats, which upset them so much that they began fighting among themselves, where formerly they had been friends." Miss Moore of Wellington, who tells the story, adds, "We became tired of this and decided that the one who was the cause of it must be put away. So we took him in a car, through the town and nearly a mile over the bridge where, near a stream, we set him free. In about three months he was back. We have always wondered how he knew that he must either cross the bridge or swim the river. He was in excellent condition, not in the least worn out, but felt as if he had been made of wood, he was so hard. One might fancy he knew why he had been strayed, for he behaved himself for a long time, taking all the unfriendly looks of the other cats in good part, and before his former enemy died, he actually gave him a caress."*

*We suspect that the explanation of this cat's changed conduct lay

In the second case a Connecticut farmer was presented with two white kittens which he named Tom and Jerry. Jerry was killed by an automobile in front of the house and the farmer's wife took Tommy out to see him. "I do not know," says this farmer, Mr. Herman Yaple, "if it made any difference, but he keeps off the road and is very much afraid of cars. Mrs. Yaple says it is on account of her taking him out to see his brother."*

Mivart said, "The cat has memory, imagination, power of sensible perception and of associating images in complex mental pictures which are more or less associated with pleasurable and painful feelings. It dreams, nor is it impossible that when cosily sitting before a cheerful fire enjoying the heat it loves so well, it may be indulging in 'day dreams' also. It associates a painful feeling with the image of the person that has hurt it."

Miss Leora Wilson tells us that her cat, Bob, on hearing the voice or merely the laugh of the veterinarian in whose care he had been placed once or twice, instantly vanished under the stoop.

Mrs. Henry Simon has her twenty cats inoculated once a year against distemper and gastro-enteritis. She says, "Although the veterinarian comes but once a year, as soon as he steps out of his car and talks to me outside the kennel, all the cats recognize him and almost go into fits. They run under tables, chairs, in corners, or any place to hide. None of my cats are a bit nervous as my kennel is on the main

---

in his happiness at being provided for once more, in the only place which he regarded as home; *i.e.,* his feelings were of gratitude rather than contrition.

*In this case the cat may have smelled the rubber from the automobile tire on the body of his brother and thereafter associated rubber with injury and death.

highway and men, women, and children stop in cars to come in the kennel and see the cats; and all these same cats that are so afraid of this veterinarian run to all the strangers that come in to see them."

The most intelligent animals are those that use their fore paws as hands. As described in chapters on Physiology, and Voice and Language, the cat does this in many ways. Some of its most remarkable feats are rattling door knobs, opening doors and windows, and ringing bells.

MECHANICAL ABILITY

Romanes mentioned the cat's remarkable understanding of mechanisms. Only the apes form associations as rapidly and they are not capable of the same concentration.

A cat owned by a friend of the author discovered that by turning the catch on one of the kitchen windows she could let herself out. The rope was broken and when the catch was released the upper sash dropped. She regularly reached the yard in this manner.

Miss Jean Seivwright says, "A neighbor had a bell hung onto her door with a strap attached, and when the cats wanted to get inside the house, they used to go and ring it."

Miss Lucy G. Wolfe says, "Spunky can open doors, and time after time I have found him in the attic when the door has been tight shut. Our neighbor two doors away found him under her bed yesterday and all her doors were shut, and she has found him in her cellar several times. If he wants to get in a room and cannot quite manage the latch, he will stand on his hind legs and bat the door knob with one paw, causing it to rattle violently until some one lets him in."

Thomas Tiptail, a twenty-four-pound cat owned by Mrs.

Elizabeth Becker of Ossining, New York, rattled the big knob on the main door until his summons was answered, and his delight in his performance was evident.

Miss Edna Hopkins informs us that a family cat, Silver Bell, knew that his salmon was kept in the cellar way, the door of which had a wooden fastening with a string attached to pull the door open. He formed the habit of jumping on a near-by table and pushing the button around with one paw while he pulled the string with the other. Miss Hopkins says, "We had to change the lock. He had used his keen eyes to advantage."

Charles Dudley Warner's cat, Calvin, opened the register when he wanted more heat, but never closed it.

Mrs. Beatrice Greig tells us that she taught her black hybrid Siamese, Tiddle-dee, to lie with his head and fore paws on her right arm when she suffered from neuritis in that arm, and he does this for hours without moving, but he likes to go out at about 5 A.M., and evolved a clever trick. In the room is a window which opens out in two halves fastened by a bolt in the center. On two occasions Mrs. Greig found the window open and could not understand it until one morning she awoke, hearing a "click-phlop," and looking under the mosquito curtain saw the cat sitting on the sill, lifting the bolt with his paw and holding it while he shoved the half open sufficiently to let himself out.

Anna Botsford Comstock, describing a cat she owned when a child, says it opened a door from the thumb-piece side by reaching up and throwing one front leg through the handle, thus supporting its weight while it pressed down on the thumb-piece with the other front foot. In this manner the cat would swing into the room on the door, much to the amazement of visitors.* A cat can also open such a door when it swings outward, and in this case has been observed to throw one fore leg through the handle and press on the thumb-piece with the other, while kicking against the framework at the side with its hind legs, thus forcing the door open.

The dog is quick to profit by the cat's superior mechanical ability, and to rush into the house when its feline friend succeeds in opening the door.

It will be seen from the foregoing authenticated incidents that the cat learns to open doors and windows principally by its powers of observation, and occasionally by the trial-and-success method. It has also other means of accomplishing an end. Louis Wain's cat, in the middle of the night, lifted a corner of the door mat and let it fall back in place until he had attracted attention and the door was opened to admit him. A cat of the author's, in the middle of the night, climbed up the screen door at the front of the house, pulling hard at the wires and shaking the door. She never climbed the screen door at the rear of the house, knowing that our room was so situated that we would hear her better at the front door. During the day, when the front door (inside the screen door) stood open, she gently hooked a few wires of the screen door repeatedly to apprise us of her presence, but did not climb the door or attempt to shake it. Harriet, Miss Florence Carter's cat, who is fond of red, wakes early, and in order to rouse her mistress picks up a weight attached to the radio ground wire and tosses it noisily about. If this fails to bring action, she walks on the piano keys.

Flying Silver Cloud, a pedigreed silver Persian owned by

*The Pet Book, 1914.

Mrs. Edith W. Berwyn, rattles the door by standing on his hind legs and striking it rapidly with one paw after the other; and Mittens, the property of Mr. and Mrs. S. H. Kay of East Walpole, Massachusetts, rattled the key of the door and gave three taps on the window when wishing to enter the house.

A black-and-white cat appropriately named Smarty, a large and handsome animal owned by Mrs. Charles Wester of Carmel, New York, opened doors by taking the knobs between his paws and turning them; and he tipped the push bell on the front door when he wished to go in. At first Mrs. Wester was puzzled when the bell rang and she found no one at the door but the cat, but she soon discovered that Smarty was pushing the button.

One cat pushed the button, then looked to see if any one were responding, and if not he pushed again, which proves that a cat's ringing the bell is not done merely because of a chance discovery that pressing on a certain spot causes the door to open, but that there is thought behind the act.

EXPERIMENTAL METHODS OF STUDYING CATS

The experimental method in comparative psychology was first applied to cats. Thorndike did the original work in this field (1897–98) and understood his cats so little that they were greatly excited during the experiments. His wrong technique naturally led to wrong conclusions, yet his work stood until 1915, and despite their inaccurate interpretations these first psychological experiments with cats led to much improved methods in the teaching of children.

The maze, the puzzle box, the colored lights, and other paraphernalia of the modern psychological laboratory frequently lead to such ridiculous conclusions that it seems certain that the following information given in two modern children's encyclopedias (1936 and 1937) must have been derived from some such source:

White cats with pink eyes (albino cats) are nearly always deaf.
Cats see well in the dark.
They have treacherous instincts.
A cat is not always a good pet for a child.

Another encyclopedia of 1914, whose information evidently was derived from the same source, says:

A few [cats] have been trained to hunt but none to retrieve.
Dogs exceed them in the understanding of mechanical appliances.
Ninety-nine per cent of male tortoise-shell kittens are red tabbies.*

The facts of the foregoing statements are these:

Albino cats are not deaf.
Cats cannot see in the dark.
Cats do not have treacherous instincts, unless these are developed by cruel treatment.
A cat is always a good pet for a normal child properly instructed in kindness to animals.

Cats are natural retrievers and need no training in this respect.
Dogs are not so clever as cats in the understanding and manipulation of mechanical appliances.
Male tortoise-shell kittens are marked exactly the same as the females. A red tabby is an entirely different cat.

One scientific experimenter states that he had treated a kitten roughly the day before and it seemed afraid of him.

*In one of our foremost encyclopedias for adults the cat article contains ten misstatements.

No one with a knowledge of cats needs to be told that this man's experiments would be of small value. The mind of the cat cannot be judged accurately by those who lack a sympathetic understanding of the animal, and except by people with such understanding it never will be judged correctly in a laboratory. The cat is like the genius:

> For sparks electric only strike on souls electrical alike.
> The flash of intellect expires unless it meets congenial fires.

Donald Keith Adams astutely points out that "It is a common failure of comparative psychologists to compare the behavior of experienced human beings with that of inexperienced animals," and adds, "The inference of mind should be made to require similarity of past experience as well as of structure, situation, and behavior." He accords to the cat the possession of practical ideas, articulate ideas, and foresight, that is, the ability to put two and two together, and he noticed that one success accomplishes perfect learning.

MEMORY

The strength of a cat's memory of an event or of a person depends largely upon the intelligence of the cat, the age of the cat, and what has happened since the event occurred or the person last was seen. Cats also differ in point of memory the same as people.

Miss Edna M. Hopkins tells us that when, after an absence of six months, she returned to a home in Massachusetts where she had been in the habit of tossing a rubber ball up and down the stairs for the cat, Buddie, to retrieve, the cat, on seeing her, immediately ran for his ball and carried it to her at the foot of the stairs.

Hudson states that a cat remembered him after an absence of six months: "She came to a sudden stop on the threshold, stared at me for two or three seconds, dashed across the room and jumped onto my knee and began vigorously to lick my hand."

Hermie, a kitten reared by the author, when seven months old was placed in a country home where he was obliged to become accustomed to an entirely different kind of life, and he remembered us for only a limited time. From life in an exceedingly quiet home, with a small family, no radio or dogs, he was transferred to a home where the family consists of six people, three of whom are men, two cats, a large dog, and a radio; and as he was not allowed out of the house for a week or more lest he attempt to return to his former home, the distraction must have been keen. It was a great deal to ask a little cat to learn amid such confusion, but he speedily discovered that the lady of the house loves and feeds him and the other folks are kind and pet him, that the old cats are not difficult to get on with, that the collie adores cats and allows them to play with his tail; and so he settles down, purrs, and accepts the new conditions as gracefully as possible. When we visited him seven months later he knew us immediately and lay at our feet. As we sat with one hand hanging, he took one of our fingers in his paw and gripped it with his toes in gentle recognition. A year later, though still more friendly than with strangers, he seemed a little uncertain as to our identity, and still another year after that he accepts us only as a pleasant incident. We offer him puffed wheat and it appears to stir some pleasant recollection in his brain, but he cannot recall his kittenhood nor connect the puffed wheat with his old home, for that now is not even a memory.

Most cats that have remembered well a loved member of a household for a long period of months, or even for several years, were those that have remained in the same familiar surroundings, and it was not they but the loved one who withdrew. In these cases memory requires nothing more than fitting the person back into the place he previously occupied, and this is relatively easy.

A cat has been known to grieve for another cat for two years and to remember an intentional injury for the same length of time. When a young puss, Tweetie Heart (described in chapter on Longevity) was severely reprimanded by her owner, and for nearly two years she purposely avoided him; but cats appear to forgive and forget an unintentional injury, particularly if soothed at the time.

Warner's cat, Calvin, remembered him after an absence of two years.

Mrs. Wynne Allen was away from home for two years, during which time her sister cared for her cat, Potty. On Mrs. Allen's return the cat (described in chapter on Longevity) not only remembered her, but immediately remembered his old habit of sleeping on her bed, though he never slept on her sister's bed.

Mrs. Genevieve F. Davidson of Yonkers, New York, was obliged to break up her home and move south, and her cat, Boots, was taken by Mrs. William G. Rogers and well cared for. This cat, a very reserved animal, never made friends with strangers. After four years Mrs. Davidson made a journey north, during which she visited Mrs. Rogers. Boots knew her at once, jumped in her lap, made a great fuss over her and had no eye for any one else during the several days that she remained. After her departure he went to her room, sought everywhere for her, and cried at Mrs. Rogers as though to say, "Where is she?"

Amos, owned by Mrs. D. G. Rosenberger of Elkins Park, Pennsylvania, when about a year old was taken by his mistress to call on a friend whose mother cat chased him and frightened him badly. He has never forgotten or forgiven the woman who owned the mother cat. Whenever he meets her, whether in her home or his, he flies into a temper and spits and growls at her, though he never acts in this manner toward any other person and under all other circumstances exhibits a most lovable disposition. He has done this for seven years, though six months sometimes elapse between visits. It cannot be due to the odor of the mother cat, for the woman has owned no cats for several years. (This, of course, is a case of revived memory.)

Mrs. Beatrice Greig tells us that when her daughter had to leave home to go to school, the parting from her adored tortoise-shell, Kittyboy, was heartbreaking. "And when children came to the house the cat's joy and excitement were pathetic to watch. However, she lived to see Irene return after six years and knew her at once. Irene was broken-hearted at leaving her loved school and did a lot of weeping over it, and Kittyboy used to lie beside her and wipe away her tears with her paw."

From these facts it appears that the cat's maximum sustained memory is six years. (See also p. 189.)

Our chapter on Longevity shows that cats seldom lose their memory with age, but Snowball, we are told by Miss Linda M. French, seemed to lose her memory before she was ten years old. "She would have kittens and forget to go near them for days at a time," says Miss French. "We had to drown two or three litters to prevent them from starving. Later on she would remember them and hunt for them."

Lafcadio Hearn thought the cat's memory of the present life not so good as its racial memory—"the memory of experiences accumulated through countless billions of lives" —which he thought was vivid and seldom at fault.

CONCENTRATION

In several respects the cat is more like ourselves than is any other animal, not only in its rare sense of humor, for example, but also in its power of concentration and in individual differences of character. A child can be made to forget what it had in mind by having its attention diverted, but a cat cannot be made to forget.

One test of intelligence is the ability to pay attention and concentrate. The cat ranks high in this respect. We have all seen a cat watch for hours at a mouse hole. An excellent example of this great power of concentration is sent us by Doctor Emmeline Moore of Albany, New York: "Our neighbor had a beautiful golden yellow tabby whose concentration was so great that when in winter he foraged for mice in a neighboring cornfield, he found himself frozen to the stubble watching for his prey. Eventually he disentangled himself and carried home ice attached to his body and feet with stubble included."

IMITATIVE ABILITY

Mother cats often teach their kittens by setting them an example, which the kittens copy. (Hence, no doubt, the children's expression, "copy cat.") They teach their kittens how to dispatch a rat, and if they themselves have been taught not to molest birds, will train their young not to molest them. Grown cats also imitate one another and some imitate people. Cats belonging to engine companies often imitate their masters by sliding down the pole whenever the fire bell rings. On board a steamer when the men paraded every day for drill, the ship's cat always stood at the end of the line. One cat watched a post hole being dug in the garden, then, planting her hind feet firmly on the edge of the hole, dug and scratched with her front paws. (This was construed as an effort to help, but may have been nothing more than imitation.) A cat described by Sarah B. Wister imitated her human friends by wiping her feet on the door mat before entering the house, and Louise Chandler Moulton's cat, Richard Cœur de Lion, wagged his tail whenever the dog did, but never did so after the dog died.

If a kitten has ascended a tree and is fearful of coming down, its mother will go up and show it how to descend, and a male cat will do the same in the case of a timid friend. Miss Isa A. De Pledge of Oneida, New York, tells us that when the weather was quite cold and immense snowbanks covered the grounds, a strange dog chased a black cat, Gypsy, up a tree, and no amount of coaxing served to bring it down. A big dog, Keno, who was Gypsy's friend, would stand under the tree and try to coax it down, then the yellow cat, Laddie, would run up the tree almost to where Gypsy was sitting and back down slowly, repeating this performance a number of times; but the black cat was too thoroughly frightened to descend, and after two days and two nights was rescued by the fire department. A striped female kitten described by Miss Grace A. Petersen of Richmond Hill, New York, having climbed into a grapevine trellis, was afraid to come down, and a yellow-and-white male cat climbed up and showed her how to descend. She understood, but was too timid to imitate him, whereupon he went behind her and gave her a gentle push, which compelled her to begin the descent. Miss Petersen describes a young kitten which she taught how to climb stairs, and which, next morning, took all its brothers and sisters and showed them how to climb the stairs.

A small back-yard city cat observed by the author was very gentle and would fight no other cat but only intrude his head shyly into a dish set down expressly for him and appropriated by others. But one day an older cat took him by the head with both paws, claws out, and screamed at him, and after that the young cat took other cats by the head with his claws out and screamed at them, attacking any tom cat larger than himself if he thought it was stealing favors intended for him. At such times his face took on a fierce expression like that of a cat that has to fight its own way.

A short-haired brown tabby owned by the author commonly was allowed only a small saucer of water at night because of her habit of splashing it over the floor. Often she had noticed that when she splashed water on the floor a mop was withdrawn from a kitchen cabinet, the drawer of which would not close, and the water sopped up with it. One night a basin of water was inadvertently left on the floor, and the next morning, when the door was opened, the cat did not come to greet us as usual. She had gone to the cabinet, secured a mop by thrusting her paw in the partly open drawer, and with it in her teeth was treading back and forth through the puddle. She did not carry the mop as a cat carries a snake or large lizard, at one side, but by straddling.

SENSE OF HUMOR

No one who has ever watched a kitten at play doubts the fine sense of humor that is inherent in the domestic cat, a quiet but effervescing and contagious merriment. To the young cat life is a circus and he the clown.

The cat loves to tease other cats and also dogs. It will tease a dog by the hour, making the canine look very foolish indeed. We once saw a cat reposing on a fence which abutted on a strip of open ground. A fox terrier saw the cat and leapt toward it, barking furiously. The cat instantly perceived that the terrier could not reach it and remained where it was, not once again looking at the dog, though it looked over and beyond him, and the stupid animal continued to leap up and bark wildly for fully an hour. All this time the cat, half dozing, fanned the canine's excitement by dangling its tail over the fence and keeping it in rhythmic motion. When the terrier finally went away, the overworked muscles at the rear of his neck were bunched into a sizable hump. A cat seldom makes the same mistake twice, and in such case would have desisted after one effort.

Laddie and his dog companion, Keno, play together like a pair of kittens, says Miss De Pledge. When Keno was asleep one day Laddie thrust out his paw and tickled Keno on the nose, repeating this performance until he roused the dog. Miss Phyllis A. Bowne of Floral Park, New York, tells us how Aloysius teases the neighbor's dog, a wire-haired terrier. When the cat notices that the dog is tied in the back yard, which adjoins his own, he takes great delight in running up and down and around and around his yard, then observing the effect on the dog. As Miss Bowne interprets it, Aloysius is trying to convey the idea, "You are tied up, but I can go where I please, and am I having fun!"

The late Mr. William Greig of Trinidad had a cat named Dillo, a beautiful black half-Persian who traveled with him in his own traveling box and always slept on his bed. One night Mr. Greig missed the cat, called all over the house in vain, took a lantern and searched the grounds, and, says Mrs. Greig, "returned miserably to his room, where he found Dillo on the top of his mosquito net looking over and laughing at him."

Harriet also likes to tease and fool people. Says Miss Carter, "There are two apartments on the first floor, and one night Harriet teased to be let out the front door of her home. She then ran around to the front door at the other side of the house and teased to be let in. This kept up until both occupants compared notes and decided it to be deliberate foolery."

Gentle teasing of this sort is something the cat greatly enjoys, and it likes to be gently teased itself; but rough teasing will ruin the temper of the sweetest cat. One cat even resented being mimicked, and slapped a woman who was trying to imitate its cry. A female kitten was kept in a city flat by a family in which the man thought it amusing to tease the animal, inciting her to rage and doubtless inflicting pain. When she grew to cathood she attacked the man who, despite his brute strength, was afraid to be alone

Photograph by Mrs. Edith W. Berwyn

The cat is emotional, moody, and sometimes haughty. This shaded silver queen, Dulcie Curitza, is owned by Mrs. Elbert Fenn of San Diego, Calif.

Top: Nebuchadnezzar, posed on the post before Mrs. Becker went for a walk, followed her but was always on the post when she returned. *Bottom:* Harriet (Carter) gets attention in the early morning by tossing the radio ground wire or walking on the piano keys.

with her. She also attacked every other man who entered the apartment, and it became necessary to have her destroyed.

Most felines dislike to be dressed up or ridiculed, but there are occasional exceptions in cats that greatly enjoy wearing ornaments, and in some in which the sense of humor is so keen that they can appreciate a laugh on themselves. Harriet loves to wear a harness, but growls if a leash is attached to it. Mrs. Alfred Nocka's cat, William, (chapter on Longevity) loved his plaid cap and gown, and, she says, "would rather pose than eat." An English cat, Sandy, described in the *Spectator*,* allowed the children to dress him up and was much pleased when everybody laughed. We have known two neuter cats that were exceedingly happy when attired in a doll's bonnet, but we suspect their pleasure derived not so much from wearing the contraption as from the expressions of human approval which followed its adjustment. It must be remembered also that Egyptian cats wore earrings and jewelled collars.

STRATEGY

The strategy of the cat is one of its most remarkable mental attributes. Mivart describes a cat that tried in vain to catch a starling, then got on a cow's back and waited until the cow approached the birds, when he was able to secure one without difficulty. Romanes says that cats have been seen to scatter crumbs in order to attract birds for which they then waited in ambush, and a celebrated cat named Joe, of the Board of Taxes, London, carried a news-

*Quoted in *The Living Age,* May 1, 1915, p. 316.

paper to a spot frequented by pigeons and hid under it for an opportunity to seize the unsuspecting prey. Thus he sometimes captured two in an hour.

Mrs. Elizabeth Becker says she used to pose Nebuchadnezzar on the gate post when she started for a walk, telling him to remain there until she came back. He invariably followed her, playing at keeping out of sight in the bushes and skulking along stone walls, but was always on the post when she returned. Twice she saw him swiftly mounting the post, taking the same pose in which she had left him, and looking enormously pleased with himself.

Dillo would meet his master when the latter returned from work and accompany him up-stairs, and just as Mr. Greig was about to slip into his easy chair, Dillo would get there first. This bit of strategy never staled. Mrs. Greig tells us that once she had a charming yellow cat named Rufus who slept on her bed every night and was in the same place when she woke in the morning. She says, "He never knew that I knew that when I fell asleep he went out and did not return until the psychological moment."

The sharp wits of the stray tom cat who has succeeded in maintaining himself often have been noted. One recent winter, during a spell of extremely bitter weather, the author entered a store one evening, and with us there slipped in a hardened, nonchalant old tom cat. He walked straight to the radiator and sat down to warm himself. The wants of the other customers having been supplied, we dragged out the time as long as possible, certain that when we left the cat would go too, for he understood perfectly that he would not be made welcome by the proprietor. As we expected, he walked out with us and disappeared, his back a little warmer and with that much gained in the desperate struggle for survival.

KNOWLEDGE OF TIME

Cats, on numerous occasions, have been known to distinguish a certain hour of the day, and some observers believe they distinguish certain days of the week, but of this we have no evidence.

Beatrice Portinari, who always went to the front window in the morning when she saw us about to leave the apartment and watched us go up the street, knew when it was time for our return from work and every day, about thirty minutes before we were due, went to the door of the apartment and waited for our arrival, when she greeted us with a great show of pleasure and affection.

Doctor Cadwalader C. Vinton of New York City says, "A neighbor of mine owned Fluffy, a beautiful yellow Persian who, every afternoon in all weathers, about twenty minutes before her master's train time, seated herself in the middle of the sidewalk part way to the corner, or in snow or rain sheltered under a bush, and rode home in his arms or curled round his neck."

Chapter Twelve

"TELEPATHY AND OCCULT VISION"
IN THE CAT

"CATS," said Sir Walter Scott, "are a mysterious kind of folk. There is more passing in their minds than we are aware of." Scott recognized in cats a certain quality of mind which from the most ancient times has been called occult—a quality much observed and wondered at, and which, during the days of witchcraft, worked the animal great harm.

Spiritualists assert that the Egyptians believed the cat protected them from inimical supernatural influences and felt safe when it was in the house. A similar belief existed in Japan. From the chapter on Physiology it will be seen that there is no mystery about the cat's perception of sights and sounds which lie beyond the human range, that the animal is gifted with sensibilities more delicate than ours, and that these sensibilities, like many other animal phenomena, are as yet not wholly understood. The strong reluctance on the part of many scientific men to grant that the cat even has a mind carries conservatism to an unwarranted extreme, admits a lack of careful investigation of the obviously unusual psychology of the animal, and necessitates a denial of the countless authenticated examples of the cat's ability to think. Perhaps this negative or skeptical attitude is due in part to the layman's error in bending the bough too far in the direction of the mysterious and inexplicable when describing the qualities of the cat. The powers of its small brain, amazing though they are, have been grossly exaggerated, and a profundity entirely beyond its scope assigned to it. While Occidentals stated that it has "nearly all knowledge," Chinese declared that it can mark on the ground and divine its prey, also that it possesses an insight into the past, exhibited by greater friendliness for persons born in the same season of the year as itself; and other Orientals said that not only has the animal a language of its own and an extreme acuteness which enables it to perceive objects *and beings* invisible to man, but that it possesses a knowledge of the future.

The cat's habit of looking a person steadily in the eye, not observed in other animals, has given it the rank of a peculiarly knowing, not to say penetrating, animal. Its understanding of the mental and physical states of people it loves, and its sympathy with them in sickness and sorrow, are notable. Its habit, called meditative, of sitting with eyes half closed, as though seeing something beyond us, and its remarkable intuition, have given it a clairvoyant aura in the eyes of the layman. Its foreknowledge of changes in the weather, of earthquakes, the approach of friends and social functions, and of the death of animals and people is undeniable, but without doubt in each case the phenomenon has a physical explanation.

Though cats in our presence sometimes appear to divine our intentions, instances of telepathy are rare. W. H. Hudson, who abhorred sentimentalism and exaggeration with respect to animal phenomena, believed the story of a woman who, having left her cat to be cared for by a gardener while she was settling in a new home, had three visions in one night of the cat on a wall starved nearly to death. So vivid was the impression in the morning that she went at once to the old home, where she found that the gardener had been dismissed and the cat had run to the wall where it was nearly dead. She had arrived just in time to save its life.

Some occultists declare that they are able to convey to a cat the thought that it must come to them, and though in deep slumber it will respond. The subject of telepathy still is so far from plumbed that we can only quote these claims, for future elucidation or disproof.

Many people whose vision is good for specters or "astral photographs impressed on the psychic atmosphere," declare that they have seen the apparitions of cats (as well as of horses, pigs, and other animals). To most of us, however, cat ghosts are somewhat like the shades of the famous Kilkenny cats:

> Their ghosts are here; but all so thin
> They can't be heard, or felt, or seen.

It has been stated that cats have seen ghosts at the same time that certain people have seen them, and since there are people apparently gifted with seeing spirits, some cats may be similarly endowed. The "spirits" may represent natural phenomena which in time may be visible to every one, whether *Homo sapiens* or *Felis catus*.

Cats present at seances are said to be uneasy and fearful, but not much weight can be attached to this unless we know where the seances are held. Naturally they would be uneasy and fearful in a strange place.

FOREKNOWLEDGE

Of the Weather: Since time immemorial cats have been observed to act queerly in one way or another before a change in the weather. In the seventeenth century it was believed that if they put the foot beyond the crown of the head in washing, it would rain, and that era yields many quaint sayings, such as "A cat 'bawling' is a sign of rain"; "A cat washing her face toward the quarter that the wind is coming from, or an old cat frisking about the house at night like a kitten, foretells a storm"; "When she sits with her back to the fire, frost is coming"; "If she sleeps with her brains to the ground, it will rain within twenty-four hours," etc.

A cat described by Svend Fleuron* predicted rain by walking about shaking himself, dragging his tail, and mewing continuously; but if a pleasant day were in prospect he carried his tail perpendicularly and purred happily.

Jonathan Swift observed, though not without a touch of satire,

> While rain depends, the pensive cat gives o'er
> Her frolics, and pursues her tail no more.

C. H. Lane† says that before a snowstorm the cat is hard to waken and diffuses an odor like cloves. We do not know whether any one else has observed this phenomenon.

From the foregoing it will be seen that cats with the ability to prophesy the weather have a variety of ways of doing so. A cat with a most remarkable meteoric sense

*Kittens: A Family Chronicle, 1920.
†Rabbits, Cats and Cavies, 1903.

was Napoleon, who belonged to Mrs. Fanny H. de Shields
of Baltimore, Maryland. When rain was near this cat rested
prone on the floor, front paws extended and head between
paws, _i.e.,_ with his "brains to the ground." After a drought
of about forty days in 1930 the animal was observed in this
position, though the local paper, quoting official reports,
announced "Continued dry." Mrs. de Shields telephoned the
paper that it would rain within twenty-four hours because
Napoleon was predicting. Rain fell as the cat foretold, and
thereafter the paper published his prophecies. He never
made a mistake. The position taken by this cat is nearly
like that of a cat which appears to be suffering from head-
ache, and perhaps the atmospheric pressure or its release
actually caused his head to ache. Mrs. de Shields informs
us that he never suffered from rheumatism. He appeared to
have no foreknowledge of other events such as the death
of a human being or an animal. He lived to be nearly
nineteen years old, and his tombstone in Aspin Hill Cemetery for Pet Animals, Rockville, Maryland, bears his picture with the inscription, "Napoleon, the Weather Prophet,
1917–1936."

It is impossible to tell in what way the elements affect
cats, aside from the supposed sensitiveness of the fur and
vibrissæ to meteoric conditions.

Of Earthquakes: That cats are peculiarly sensitive to vibrations is illustrated by the fact that deaf ones can be summoned by tapping on the floor. One deaf cat always came
when a stringed instrument was played, sensing the vibrations immediately. A heavy atmosphere is believed to be
the forerunner of an earthquake, though human beings do
not always associate the two phenomena. Cats notice it, and

Napoleon Predicting

C.C.H

Top: Napoleon the Weather Prophet predicting rain. From a
drawing made by Miss Charlotte C. Hulme in 1931. *Bottom:*
Photograph of the same cat. He was owned by Mrs.
Fanny H. de Shields of Baltimore, Maryland.

The black cat has been the object of much superstition, but its "occult powers" are no greater than those of other cats. The specimen shown is a Persian female, B'Tina, bred and owned by Mrs. F. M. Herms of Tarrytown, New York.

the ground vibrations which precede an earthquake are plainly felt by them. They have been observed before a shock to tremble and draw back their ears, eyes glittering and hair standing on end—indications of disapproval, fear, and excitement. They are said to mew plaintively, and a commonly told but unverified story is to the effect that they sometimes persuade their owners to follow them on such occasions out of the danger zone.

*Of the Approach of Friends and Social Functions:** At a gathering where more than twenty guests had assembled the author once met a white cat named Mannie, owned by Mrs. William G. Rogers. The cat passed through the kitchen, dining room, sitting room, and into the farthest corner of the parlor, and without noticing any other guest came directly to us and jumped on our lap as though he had had it in mind to do this on entering the house. How did he know a cat lover? This cat did many "uncanny" things, indicating a fine judgment and a knowledge of people far beyond the powers of the average cat. He was, indeed, a genius among cats.

Gordon Stables tells of a mother cat that singled him out from dozens of people on the street to get him to go to the aid of her kitten, which had fallen into a cesspool.

Our Dumb Animals relates the case of a Persian prison cat that conceived a strong affection for a woman and was inconsolable for days following her discharge. On her return to durance, he knew about it before the police van had much more than entered the gates.

Jacob A. Riis, describing Slippers, the White House cat during the administration of Theodore Roosevelt (*St. Nich-*

*"Her paw prophetic raised above her ear,
  Foretold a visit from some friend was near."

olas, January, 1908), says that he absented himself for days and weeks, but always returned to his post just before a diplomatic dinner, and that everyone seeing the cat sunning himself on the front steps knew that the cards had been sent out for the dinner.

Authenticated cases of cats disappearing from home when children and other obnoxious visitors were present and reappearing the moment the objects of their aversion had left are so numerous that it seems certain the cats were in all cases secreted sufficiently near to be aware of what was going on in the house.

A cat that was left with a veterinarian knew when his master was coming and became excited long before the door bell rang.

Miss Alice E. Aldrich of Boston, Massachusetts, tells us that a female cat on Cape Cod took a great fancy to her and one day when she and a friend walked to the beach the cat followed until they arrived at the main road, about half a mile from home, where she halted. They were gone two hours and on returning to the spot where they had left the cat they found her waiting for them, but on reaching home they learned that she had been at home during the intervening time. The cat therefore walked about two miles in all. It is evident that she somehow knew that her friend was returning and went to meet her.

We are obliged to state these incidents with scant explanation, for it is impossible with our present limited knowledge of the feline mind to know what faculty it is that gives the animal this (to us) singular foreknowledge of certain events. Perhaps the principle involved is similar to that of radio transmission, and man some day may discover it. Perhaps it is an unknown sense akin or supplementary to the sense of smell, and the same sense may operate in homing.

Of Death: Doctor W. L. Clark, veterinarian, tells us that Tommy Clark, described in the chapter on Longevity, always knew when a horse was going to die, and stayed away from the hospital until the animal had been removed. The peculiar odor and actions of a horse fatally ill were, he believes, discerned by the cat.

Mr. Thomas H. Howley of New York City informs us that when his younger brother was ill the family cat, which was exceedingly devoted to the child, left the house. The boy died two days later. The cat never returned though he was seen afterward in the neighborhood. (See also p. 238.)

Instances have been recorded in which a cat knew for several weeks beforehand that its own death was approaching. Another case in point is that of David, a black-and-white cat owned by Mrs. William F. Palmer of Albany, New York. This cat had a tumor in the ear which was removed by a veterinarian who found it deep-seated. Later, when Mrs. Palmer was preparing to leave for the summer holidays, the cat would not remain in his bed but went to her repeatedly, with uncommon manifestations of affection. She remarked that it seemed as though he were saying good-by forever. He died at the veterinarian's just before her return two weeks later.

THE CAT IN WITCHCRAFT

The days of the persecution and torture of the cat along with the witch have passed with much other human wickedness, though the belief in witch cats is said to be by no means extinct among European peasantry. A witch without a broom and a cat would not be a witch. The association of the cat with witchcraft doubtless was due not only to the intelligence and uncommon properties of the creature and the habitual human failure to understand it, but to its nocturnal habits and glittering eyes, its ability to fix the human eye, the electricity of its fur, its supposed value in medicine, and possibly its unearthly wailings.

Even in modern times people sometimes express fear of an animal that seems over-intelligent. Charles Dudley Warner says, "Bertha said she sometimes was afraid of him [Calvin], he looked at her so intelligently"; and a college professor in biology once told the author that she was afraid of her horse because he looked at her so intelligently. It is not difficult, therefore, to understand that as the ignorant held witches in terror and held cats in terror, and witches and cats liked each other, the two were believed to be of the same kidney, and the fate accorded to one was meted out to the other. One of the favorite tricks of a witness in a witchcraft trial was to swear that he had seen the devil himself in the form of a cat, and the judges themselves were too credulous and superstitious to inquire how the witness knew that the cat was the devil. Testimony regarding repercussion was also given freely and accepted with equal gullibility. In such cases a cat sustained an injury and soon afterward an old woman was found to have the same injury. This proved her to be a witch, capable of assuming the form of a cat.

The witch's cat was supposed to speak the language of its mistress. Addison describes a witch, Moll White, whose tabby cat was reputed to have talked in English on several occasions.

PART THREE

THE BEHAVIOR OF THE CAT

Character
Sexes
Emotions
Habits
Instincts

Chapter Thirteen

THE CHARACTER OF THE CAT

CERTAIN TRAITS in the domestic feline are nearly uniform, others, good and bad, are brought out solely by environment; and cat breeders and others who have observed many cats are unanimous in stating that they have not found two alike in temperament and character. Each cat is a law unto itself.

People who have disliked cats and altered their views generally explain their conversion by saying, "This is not a cat. It is a personality."

Personality is defined by C. A. Barnicoat* as "the power to fascinate and repel," and he adds, "No animal possesses this power in so high a degree as the cat."

It fascinates in a variety of ways, each feline addict giving a different reason for yielding to its fascinations: it is a great solace to a lonely soul; it is soothing and calm; it is polite and tidy and the only suitable four-footed companion for the library, the dining room and the parlor; it is good company on all occasions; it is sympathetic and understanding; its electricity is stimulating; the softness of its coat is a sensuous joy; it is an aid in convalescence; each individual differs so materially from all others that it affords a continuous pleasant surprise and one never can have too many cats; it is so little trouble compared with dogs and

*"The Cat and the Human," *Temple Bar*, n. s., v. 2, p. 162, 1906.

other pets; it repays in countless grateful ways the small
care it entails; there is psychic contagion in its merriment;
it is an ornament to any home; it is art and music combined; it is sweet, sensitive, and much more clever than
most people; its beauty elevates the mind, etc.

It repels also in a variety of ways. Many people deeply
resent its intelligence, its independence, its insolence, its
silence, dignity, and serenity, its refusal to make friends with
those it deems unworthy of its trust, and its determination
to preserve its poise and its entity under any and all circumstances. The cat's willfulness has militated against a general recognition of its virtues and sagacity. It is perverse,
nervous, timid though no coward, resentful of ill-usage,
and a hater of the rough, the loud, and the boisterous. It is
an emotional and moody creature, sometimes haughty even
toward those it loves. To many the character of the animal
is baffling and its ways inexplicable.

This unobtrusive small feline is self-sufficient, proud, a
perfect egotist, a past master of sublime detachment, high-
strung, vain, and often the center of its own universe. It is
home-loving, neat, orderly, refined and well-mannered, resourceful, patient, persevering, consistent. To those who
have won its good will it is entertaining, gracious, lovable,
ingratiating though never fawning, and essentially comforting; an animal both useful and ornamental. With understanding treatment its best qualities are brought out, its individual traits of character are developed, and it becomes
indeed a unique personality.

The cat is called a complex animal, but it is more con-
tradictory than complex, and its nature is reflected from
many facets:

It purrs so rhythmically—and caterwauls so discordantly.
It is so quiet and comforting—and so noisy and disturbing.
It tears a rival's ear—and helps him in distress.
It caresses so affectionately—and spits, and snarls and scratches.
It dislikes to be taught tricks—but teaches itself tricks.
It is so cruel—and so benevolent.
It kills a mouse—or if motherless will suckle it.
It comes instantly when called—or walks the other way.
It dislikes to wet its feet—but goes into the water to fish.
It is called a carnivore—but has a taste for fruits and vegetables.

Some of these contradictions are due to human influence. Often the cat is what we make it. The cat is not sly, treacherous, sneaky, spiteful, or suspicious unless its human associates have made it so. A cat that has been grossly abused or has sustained a physical injury entailing the loss of a foot or the crippling of a leg is apt to be irascible; otherwise the animal, with rare exceptions, is exceedingly good-natured when kindly managed. Some cats do not care for petting and an occasional cat, however well treated, is not sweet-tempered. Temperament and habits differ with breed but not, as is commonly believed, with color, though they appear to be influenced by heredity.

CRUELTY OF THE CAT

The cat's cruelty often is referred to. Darwin thought it a very cruel animal. It cripples a mouse or bird, and as the victim creeps or hops slowly away, runs after it and bites it again, repeating this until its prey is too nearly dead to attempt escape, when it leisurely devours it. We have not seen a cat play with a live fish, but have seen one toss a crippled, squawking sparrow into the air with the same abandon exhibited in tossing a plaything.

The cat apparently plays with a mouse or bird to amuse itself, in the same manner that it plays with a leaf, but it is quick to kill when it attacks a venomous serpent, a scorpion, a rat, or a squirrel. It knows better than to play with these.

One man says that how a cat can enjoy sticking a dozen curved pins into a mouse and playing with it for half an hour is beyond his understanding, but we suspect that he readily comprehends how a sport fisherman can play a muskallunge or swordfish on one curved pin for four hours. Possibly man acquired his cruelty by studying and improving upon the methods of the cat.

LEAVING ONE GOOD HOME FOR ANOTHER

However much they are loved, however tenderly cared for, cats will leave one home for another, either with or without a preliminary trial. If they return to the old home it is only for a cursory glance, and they never reveal the real reason for the change.

Mrs. Grace L. Emerson of North Abington, Massachusetts, tells us of several cases illustrative of this trait:

My sister in New Hampshire carried a kitten home from here and she could not keep it at all. She went after it several times and finally gave up. She gives her cats everything that they could want and thinks everything of them, so it is hard to understand why it was unhappy. She had a large black-and-white Angora. A neighbor's cat went there and had kittens, and the neighbor could not keep any of them home, so my sister adopted them. They bothered the older cat some, but in the end they lived peacefully together.

Mrs. Stetson, who lived on a farm above here, had a three-colored cat named Diddy-puss, and all the Stetsons loved her, but she would not stay at home. Diddy-puss had several kittens out by our wall and finally decided that it was too cold for them outdoors and brought them up to the barn. She would spit and snarl at my cat and try to drive her away. I told Mrs. Stetson her cat was here and they came after her. The next day she brought all her family back, and again they took her home. The kittens were carried back and forth until they were so large they would follow their mother down through the fields, over stone walls, etc. Finally the Stetsons put the kittens in a wire pen, and Diddy-puss abandoned them to stay here and tried in every way to drive my cat out and come into the house to stay. She stayed here until she died. The Stetsons conducted a large dairy and the cat was fed nice warm milk and plenty of other good food.

When we were children at home (seven in the family) a cat came to us and we all adopted it at once. A few days later a woman living about three miles away claimed it, and despite the weeping and wailing she carried it off. My brother felt especially bad. The next morning Mother called us and said she had something to show us. There on the well curb lay the cat washing up after her journey. Great joy prevailed but it was short-lived, for the woman came after the cat the next day. She evidently shut it up that time, for it was a week before it appeared again. The owner again came after it but could not find it and so the cat remained in her chosen home.

Miss Linda M. French says that her Snowball originally was a stray cat that was taken home from a corner grocery by a Mr. Austin, at whose home she lived for several years "until she suddenly decided to adopt us instead. Mr. Austin struggled to retain possession of her, carrying home a litter of kittens she had in our barn, but she persisted until he finally gave up and contented himself with some of the kittens."

Laddie, a yellow-and-white cat, spent three or four winters with Miss Sarah Hurd of Oneida, New York, while his owners went to Florida, and then decided he would like to stay all the time and did so. He was greatly afraid of men and boys, but so devoted to Miss Hurd that there were days when he would not eat unless she herself fixed his tray, and in the evening he would go up-stairs and wait for her to come. When she remained in one room reading he sat beside her, and if she went out to her desk he followed. He lived for fourteen years.

The foregoing facts prove only one thing, and that is the absurdity of the common belief that cats are more attached to places than to people. It is not impossible that the new home itself presents more attractive features from the feline viewpoint, but we believe those features include the people in it, and that it is more than probable that certain people radiate emanations which certain cats find in perfect harmony with their nature. If instead of selecting a kitten, cat lovers would permit the kitten to select them, we believe the alliance would be more certain to turn out happily.

MOODS AND EMOTIONS

Like many other folks with conflicting characteristics and high-strung natures, the cat is temperamental. We all know the animal's singular capacity for complete detachment, though we never learn exactly what is on its mind. In the case of a cat living entirely indoors, it is possible that the wandering instinct is strongly present at such times and its preoccupation due to the fact that this is thwarted. Other states of mind are induced by indoor life. The author and a friend each owned a cat that deliberately tossed vases off mantels, and in each case the cat was a female kept indoors. In the author's cat this conduct was construed as a criticism of an unsatisfactory breakfast. When amends were made, she did not visit the mantel. A study of more cases is needed on which to found a theory concerning this peculiar behavior.

The most powerful of feline emotions are curiosity, playfulness, jealousy, devotion to another animal or a kind owner, sexual emotions, parental emotions in the female, gratitude, and fear. Selfishness is a strong feline trait, despite the great charity exhibited toward other cats when in distress, whether these are friends or foes; and pugnacity is a powerful factor in the life of the normal male and of some females. Except for the charity mentioned and for occasional attachments to cats in the same home or neighborhood, the social emotions are commonly latent with respect to its own kind, and greed is almost entirely absent. A cat never is too old to play, to learn new tricks, or to lose its insatiable curiosity. Every new object in the home must be investigated, smelled, and made familiar. A package is enticing and the cat wishes to help in opening it; and in other human activities, such as gardening or going for a walk, it eagerly participates.

Its jealousy is manifested in various ways. A cat is jealous of its own rat holes, objects to having them investigated by other cats, and will drive intruders away even though they belong in the same household. Aloysius, when the family befriended a small poodle, took to the attic and remained two days, where meals were served to him. Finally he came out when the dog was not about. "An eventual meeting was inevitable," says Miss Bowne. "They had a headlong collision one afternoon. The dog barked, the cat spat with venom, then ran upstairs and sprayed every bed in the house. Of course we had to find the dog a new home." Miss Jean Seivwright tells us of the cat of her childhood in Scotland: "We walked down the avenue in the morning to escort our father part way to the train, and the cat and all the dogs would follow. But if a neighbor's dog tried to join the procession, Pussy strenuously objected, and once I saw her leap on the back of one of the strangers and claw fiercely at his eyes."

Miss Anna Nolan of Chicago describes the character of Zip:

Zip was an orange cat that I picked up when a kitten on 42d Street, New York, opposite the Public Library, where he was crying in front of a restaurant. This was in 1916. He did not like a young man who used to call on me and once when the young man moved quickly to sit beside me on the couch in order to look over some MS. I was reading, Zip growled and jumped from the floor between us. The man hated cats and resented Zip's jealousy. He was good company, this lad, and we enjoyed the same things, but when he told me I had to choose between him and the alley cat, I chose the alley cat. Zip left me to take up his home on Park Avenue, because he was annoyed by a black cat, Carranza, who lived next door. Every once in a while Zip returned through the open window to say Hello and to whip the black cat, who settled with me when he left.

We know of no instance except the following in which a cat killed another through jealousy. Mr. Maxwell E. Perkins of New Canaan, Connecticut, tells us that his two little daughters recognized in the family tom cat a distinctly evil nature, and this cat exhibited jealousy when a female Angora kitten not more than two months old was introduced into the household. The children, waking in the night, saw the cat sitting on their window ledge, and though only eight and ten years of age respectively, they suspected by the expression of his face that he had killed the kitten. Investigation proved their fears to be correct.*

Fear, like sorrow, robs a cat of its appetite; and a sudden change in its surroundings, or even the sudden removal of a familiar object in the home, sends a nervous shock through it. Its feelings are easily hurt, and one cat that was struck by a servant refused food from the servant for six weeks.

On occasion cats have been observed to hold their tempers under trying conditions, because they have the intelligence to do so when it is advantageous to themselves. A neighbor's cat that had lost one hind foot in a rat trap and was sometimes sour-natured toward the other cats, called on the author and seated herself on a chair in the kitchen. She liked our house much better than her own, but she never made much of people, sat on their laps, or invited caresses. To test her mettle we frisked her whiskers. She exercised perfect control and, holding her peace, waited to see what would happen next, at the same time putting on a curious expression as though trying to look at her own whiskers, which gave her an amusingly cross-eyed appearance. She probably was laughing at us while we were laughing at her. (This cat objected to our attempts at singing, and actually jumped on our lap and placed her paw on our lips; but she did not do this a second time, doubtless wondering what kind of creature it was that could not learn, like a cat, in one lesson.)

*The story is hardly complete without the sequel: the children buried the kitten immediately, that their baby sister might not know about it.

DEVOTION TO OWNERS

The cat, though not always demonstrative, loves deeply and like all who love deeply, it suffers deeply. On many occasions a cat has grieved itself to death over the death of a loved human being. In one case verified by the author a cat, after his mistress' death, lay at the foot of her bed, refused all food, and died there from grief and voluntary starvation. Another cat so loved his master that when the latter left home a month in advance one summer to prepare the ·summer cottage, the cat was so nearly dead from grief at the end of three weeks that the veterinarian said he could not last another week, and it was decided to take him at once to the summer cottage, though it was not certain that he would outlast the journey as he was too weak to stand and had to be laid in his traveling basket. He survived, and at sight of his idol his spirits returned so rapidly that he stood up and walked for the first time in several days. The author saw this devoted animal, a white cat, on a subsequent occasion, sitting beside his mistress on the seat of a Cape Cod bus. The object of his heart's desire sat on the seat ahead. Again and again the cat looked at the man and uttered a little cry of affection similar to that with which a mother cat greets her only kitten and which says so plainly, "You are my one and my all." But his devotion was much longer-lived than that of the cat for her kitten.

Many cat owners, having noticed the intense suffering of their cats when left to be cared for by others during their absence, now make it a point to take the cat along. Says Miss Lucy G. Wolfe,

We took Spunky with us. I was afraid he would die of homesickness away from us. He was a very good kitty in the car although for the first hour he was very restless and miserable, but finally settled down and slept the rest of the way. He became acclimated very quickly and had the time of his life. He would sit for the longest time on the sea wall watching the surf, and there were rabbits and ground hogs to chase. . . .

He recognized his home and was so glad to get back. The morning after we returned Father called me to look on the back porch and there he sat at the side of Puffy, his friend from next door, as though telling her of the wonderful place he had been and of the steamed clams he had had to eat.

Miss Edna M. Hopkins informs us that

Babe would stand on his hind legs and kiss my mother when she asked him if he wanted something. When Mother died it was pitiful to see how he mourned for her. And after I had to leave and we had a housekeeper, he ran away from home and though Father hunted hours for him he didn't appear for nearly ten days, and then was so bruised and maimed that my father mercifully put him out of his misery.

Hermie, the author's cat, when about seven months old was left alone for an entire day. A boy helper was instructed to feed and pet him morning and afternoon, but the kitten refused food and sat on the cellar board crying up at the window from which it was our custom to speak to him. When night fell he must have concluded that he had been deserted, and the keenness of his anguish can be imagined by his conduct when he heard a familiar voice calling him from the rear door. He was out of range of hearing, wandering about, no doubt, wondering what to do, but at the third call he came bounding—and laid himself across our ankles with his paws around them to hold us fast, hugging us for joy. For thirty minutes he continued this demonstration of delight, all the time refusing to touch a morsel of food though he had tasted nothing since early morning.

Cases constantly are coming to light in which the family cat, sensible of danger, has awakened some member of the family and thus saved many lives from fire, particularly in apartment houses. Miss Anna Nolan tells us that the occupants of a building in which she once lived were roused by cries of "Fire," but she was not awakened until Petty Zou scratched her, even after she had half awakened and pushed her away. "She kept scolding and scratching me," says Miss Nolan, "until I had to get up to see what was wrong with her. The place was filled with smoke and the firemen were already in the building."*

A friend of the author who warms her room in chilly weather by means of a gas heater forgot that she had shut off the pilot, and early one morning turned on the gas without using a match and went back to bed. The cats noticed the escaping gas, and one in the room and another outside combined in rattling the doorknob until they succeeded in rousing her. Though dizzy, she was able to open windows and summon aid, and the cats never left her side while the family kept her walking about until she recovered.

Miss Edna M. Hopkins tells us that Silver Bell, who was greatly attached to Mrs. Hopkins, procured aid for his loved mistress when she was taken seriously ill in the night. Mrs. Hopkins lifted the cat out of a chair, saying, "Hop down, Silver Bell, Mother's sick." The cat went to Miss Hopkins' room and roused her by walking up and down her body,

*For outstanding heroism the Mieaou Club of Holbrook, England, gives Brave Cat Awards in the form of silver chain collars and gold medallions, and the Allied Cat Lovers, Inc., of Goshen, Indiana, awards a certificate of honor, a medal or medallion.

thus enabling her to give her mother immediate attention. This cat had a remarkable capacity for putting two and two together, and living in a manufacturing town in Maine, learned that the noon whistle was followed by his master's appearance, and when it blew he ran to the window and watched until the man appeared at the top of the hill, then ran out to meet him.

Cats have been known to spring at people who attempted bodily injury to a loved master or mistress; to call attention to the whereabouts of a burglar in hiding; to fly in the face of a burglar and claw him until he yelled and was compelled to make his escape to avoid detection, and even to identify the murderer of a loved master or mistress by their actions in his presence. The ability of cats to hear sounds inaudible to the human ear has made them on occasion most serviceable "watch dogs." The mewing of Buster, the cat, to warn the guard, prevented the escape of a notorious child-slayer, Jesse Pomeroy, from the Charlestown (Massachusetts) Prison, according to newspaper accounts of the day (1912).

A cat will travel to the four corners of the earth with those it loves. Miss Alice Engel of New York City took her cat on an extensive tour which lasted two years. He greatly enjoyed watching the passing sights from the car windows and riding in jinrikishas, and, in the excessive heat of the Red Sea, Indian Ocean, and Malay Straits, appreciated the chopped ice which the Italian liner sent four or five times a day for the small ice-pack he wore on his head. His double paws doubtless augmented the ardor with which Orientals greeted him, though in Europe, also, he was made welcome, and he returned to New York with the title of Chappie the Globe Trotter.

"Many years ago," says Mrs. William C. Rankin of Cincinnati, Ohio, "we had a large black-and-white cat with a bushy tail. He knew my father's step so well that before we heard him Pete would go and stand on his hind legs by the door, waiting; and if it were night or day and my father went into the yard and whistled for him, Pete would come over the fences answering."

Says Miss Anna Nolan:

Petty Zou, even to those who disliked cats, was as much of an individual as any member of our family. She was a little white cat with gray and orange markings, and the joy of our whole family for fourteen years. Our neighbors called her "The Fairy" because she was so different from other cats. Once, when alone in the house, I had a spell of weakness from overwork together with sinusitis and a cold, and walked down a long hall coughing and choking, and before I could reach my bed, fell before it on my knees, too weak to rise. Petty Zou twittered wildly (she never meowed, but twittered like a bird) and jumped up on the bed and back to my side, urging me to get up. I was ill for a month and had coughing spells that would bring her even from her meals to fuss. We named her "The Little White Nurse" for this. . . .

When Pet died (from cancer of the breast from nursing her granddaughter even after that cat had had kittens of her own and in spite of all we could do), I was with her, talking and soothing her. After a while she purred, and I leaned over and spoke my farewell. Just before she died that little cat reached out her paw and clutched my wrist with her claw and her eyes met mine with the most comforting expression I ever saw.

Beatrice Portinari, owned by the author, in dying did much the same. As we leaned over her in sorrow she put out a paw and closed it in our palm, as much like a handclasp as a cat could give.

Mrs. Alfred Nocka informs us that William, when nervous about anything such as a thunderstorm in the night, or when Mrs. Nocka was sick, would slip his paw into her hand "as though saying that he and I were safe together. He died also with his paw in my hand."

"Catiline died in the kitchen near the stove," says Miss Linda M. French, "with my mother in attendance on him, and she said that the last time she tried to do something for him he rubbed his head against her hand and purred, as if to thank her."

The gratitude of the cat is strong and deep, and it responds with all its heart to affection and appreciation. It will put its arms around the neck of a loved person like a child and caress him. Sometimes when it receives a grateful morsel it looks its thanks before every mouthful and may be unable to eat at all until it has run repeatedly to its benefactor to assure him of its appreciation of his kindness.

BOSSING OTHER ANIMALS AND PEOPLE

The cat teaches a puppy to respect it by warning it first with an upraised paw, then scratching its nose if it fails to desist in its attentions. It sometimes compels a dog to serve it, directly or indirectly.

A friend sends us the following account:

A neighbor's dog entered the yard of a friend of mine and began to dig a hole down through the snow. My friend's cat watched it calmly until it had finished the hole, then with a wave of its paw sent the dog home, sat down on the hole, and made use of it.

A cat sometimes appoints itself the head of the animals

of the household and compels them to obey it. A neuter black-and-white Persian kitten was transferred from the author's home to another household where it was the only pet until a dog was introduced. It accepted the dog amiably enough but dominated the animal so completely that he was not permitted to go up or down stairs, in or out, unless the cat agreed. If he attempted to outwit the cat, it would block his path and chastise him.

Sir Walter Scott's Grimalkin slept in the sun with the dogs, at least one of which was a bloodhound, but assumed an ascendancy over them, and sitting on a chair as they passed out of the room, cuffed each one on the ear, which caused the gentle Scott to remark, "Our Grimalkin here reminds me by the airs of sovereignty which he assumes that he may be a great prince incognito and that he may come sometime or other to the throne." Washington Irving says this gray cat slept in Scott's bedroom and he considered it most unwise that the window was left open at night for its entrance and exit. (Ventilation was regarded as dangerous in those days.)

Says Captain Hastings Mahony of East Orange, New Jersey:

Beauty accompanied me to the trolley (about three blocks) on my way to business in the morning, and at night was sure to be waiting for me behind some hedge within sight of the house, and when I whistled he always appeared and accompanied me home. He was known to the neighbors for blocks around, favorably to those who had no dogs and unfavorably to those who had. He was boss of all the dogs in the neighborhood, especially one many times his size who always sought retreat under his mistress' porch. Beauty found great delight in bottling up the dog in this retreat and it was necessary for me to crawl under the stoop and take the cat away to allow the dog to get out. In cold weather he enjoyed a walk attached to his leash and attired in a knitted wool sweater.

Harriet runs after Miss Carter and cuffs her ankles if she passes the refrigerator without stopping when the cat thinks she should have lunch.

Henry M. Ladd in *Nature Magazine* (March, 1936), describes a cat that was fond of oyster soup and would hide under the bed of his mistress until after the servant had propped her up and left the soup with her, when he would hop on the bed and insist on having the delicacy. If she protested he would raise his paw and growl. She hated and feared him, and he knew it and took advantage of her invalidism and her folly. This is an outstanding example of unintelligent treatment of a cat. The family, instead of appreciating his brains, whipped him, and as the cat had no idea what the whipping was for, he continued the practice of taking the soup. Had the woman invited him to have some soup from his own dish when hers was brought, the intelligent animal would have loved and served and comforted her to the end of her days.

MAKING GIFTS, AND CONTRIBUTIONS TO PARTIES

In one case a grateful cat brought its owner "a mouse, a sparrow, a butterfly, and three cockroaches, all of which were carefully arranged on the mat."

A neighbor's somewhat neglected cat which the author permitted to have a kittening box in the kitchen caught a barn rat and brought it to us as soon as she was able, laying it at our feet and talking as though to say, "With my compliments." She was obviously disappointed when the rat was not appreciated and refused to eat it herself.

If there is a party in progress, the family cat may offer some contribution, and one, whenever there was a reception in the house, walked into the drawing room with a mouse as his offering.

When Mrs. Doone Burks of Georgetown, Connecticut, was decorating a Christmas tree and placing the presents beneath it, her gray-and-white cat, Mitzy, brought a chicken foot, which she deposited under the tree with the packages. (Miss Viola Irene Cooper to the author.)

An Ohio cat always contributed to the occasion when there was company, by taking things into the middle of the living room for admiration; and on one occasion horrified the little daughter of the house by triumphantly displaying a pair of her tiny pants.

A FEMININE ANIMAL

The cat almost universally is regarded as a feminine animal, though in some languages (as in French and German) there is one word for a female cat and another for a male.

Such is the feminine nature of the cat that it has been remarked that a man who hates cats seldom is fair to women, and the author heard the president of a cat club congratulate a young man who was exhibiting a cat on the fact that he did not suffer from an inferiority complex!

A cat, like a woman, loves a home and a comfortable bed. It likes a real home better than a stack of hay, and even a cold cellar is preferable to it if attached to a home. Like a woman it prefers people with gentle, kindly ways;

and its caresses are feminine as compared with the dog's noisy, boisterous greetings. It is exquisitely clean, like a woman, loves a neat dress, appreciates attention and small courtesies, is dainty, graceful, fond of perfumes and disgusted by vile odors; and it is capable of undying devotion. The feminine nature of the cat is recognized in the expression "kittenish," applied only to a woman.

DO CATS PREFER MEN?

Whether cats prefer men, women, or children, depends in many instances, though not all, on how men, women, and children have used them. Some love the entire family, some prefer the children, others the woman of the household, and still others always like men best. They are not necessarily partial to the person who feeds them, for in households where servants handle the food they frequently select as a favorite some member of the family who never offers them anything to eat. Some cats, accustomed to women, prefer them; others enjoy a change. The sex of the cat has no bearing upon its choice.

Mickey Rendell, owned by Doctor and Mrs. Maitland W. Rendell of Brooklyn, New York, prefers men and always helps to entertain men callers with his neatest tricks; but though greatly attached to Doctor Rendell, he obeys his mistress and not his master. When she says "Nice boy," he licks her arm; but if she says "Bad boy," he stands back and looks at her questioningly, trying to understand the reason for her criticism.

Our Beatrice Portinari ignored women callers but when a man called practised her most charming wiles to win his admiration—unless he were occupying her chair, in which case she sat at his feet and stared fixedly and disapprovingly at him, for like most other cats she had a strong proprietary sense.

Mrs. Walter L. Hamilton tells us that when a painter and his gang of workmen were painting and decorating her home, her cat, Beauty, remained in the room with the men who expressed themselves as complimented by her confidence.

Mills thinks the cat's resentment to ill-treatment may originally have made it unpopular with men. Possibly it helped women to understand the animal better. Myriads of men, however, also excel in an understanding of the nature of the cat, and in some London cat shows have outnumbered women as exhibitors. It was a man (Sir Walter Scott, who at first disliked cats but capitulated to their charms after acquiring his Hinse of Hinsefield) who first referred to a cat as "who."

Mrs. Florence McCaskie of New York City tells us that when she was a child traveling with her parents, she was so greatly taken with a male kitten in Alaska that arrangements were made for a sailor to care for it and deliver it to her when his ship returned to Seattle. Several months later, when she received the kitten, Juneau, it had developed a fondness for men and thereafter would have nothing to do with women. It became deeply attached to Mrs. McCaskie's father, and when, after the latter's death, Mrs. McCaskie's mother moved to smaller quarters with her daughter and the latter's companion, Juneau refused to remain in the new home. Mrs. McCaskie says:

I have always wondered whether it was because of a dislike of a new environment or hatred of a female household. Time after time I carried him in carefully covered baskets through unfamiliar streets to the new home, but each time he returned to the old neighborhood. He made no effort to enter the old house or to make friends with the new occupants, but lived as a wild animal in the vicinity. We made arrangements for his food and milk, which he took regularly, but would make friends with no one. One day his food was untouched and no one ever saw him again. He was a magnificent animal of the tiger type, beautifully marked.

Aloysius, who lives with Miss Bowne and her mother, welcomes female company and will sit on their laps; but as soon as a man enters the front door he retreats to the stairway, glares through the banisters at the visitor, and yowls like a tom cat in battle.

Cats sometimes suddenly make up their minds that they strongly approve of the man of the house and tell him so. A remarkable case in point is that of a cat described in the biography of Sir David Brewster by his daughter. The house cat one day entered the room of this eminent Scotch physicist, inventor of the kaleidoscope and author of *More Worlds Than One,* looked straight at him, jumped on his knee, placed a paw on each shoulder, and kissed him. After that the distinguished scholar fed her himself, but she disappeared for two years. Then she returned in good condition, made her way without hesitation to the study, jumped on Brewster's knee, placed a paw on each shoulder, and kissed him exactly as on the first day.

As an illustration of the great fondness which some men and some cats entertain for each other, we have the following anecdote from Mrs. McCaskie:

When I was in Bath, England, in 1935, I met a man walking near the Abbey in the heart of the town, and casually draped around his neck was a large black cat, calmly surveying the world.

The cat lay across the man's shoulders, just as a woman wears a fur piece, with the four legs hanging in front. I was so startled that I forgot to take a picture.

Mr. Charles M. Ennis of Sacramento, California, informs us that when he inspects his aquarium room, which contains fifty tanks of rare fishes, his white half-Persian cat, Snowball, accompanies him, draped about his neck. He says, "She desired to see into the tanks on which I was working and in time learned to make herself comfortable about it, simply lying down upon my neck and shoulders and relaxing as only a cat can relax. In many years she has never touched a fish. I love her, and when time for me shall be no more, she is welcome to all my fishes."

Chapter Fourteen

MALES, NEUTER MALES, AND
MOTHER CATS

MALES

A MALE cat, like a female, is grievously jealous of his post as the only pet of the household and may run away if a new cat is introduced. A beautiful, intelligent cat in New York City did this and later was found in such a pitiable condition that he was turned over to a humane society for destruction. Another case is that of Potty Allen (chapter on Longevity). When twenty years old he was deeply offended when Mrs. Allen fed a strange tom cat and before leaving the house looked nervously out at each side of the door to see if the intruder were there, and finally ran away. He was known to the entire town of Ringgold, Texas, and widely searched for, and after five weeks a man saw him crossing a street and reported to the Allens that the cat was under a garage. They drove to the spot and found him, greatly emaciated. They parted with the stranger and all was well again with the old cat.

Notable exceptions to this rule have occurred, however, one in which a young tom cat was introduced into a home where an old tom cat had always reigned supreme, and the two conceived a strong attachment for each other. The young tom brought the old one many a dainty and was inconsolable when he died.

A male cat whose owner fed also a stray cat exhibited a fine sense of fairness by taking only half the food from the dish and leaving the remainder for the stray; and if the stray came to the dish first, the owned cat waited until it had eaten half the food, then nosed in himself for the other half.

It is not known why some males are tender fathers and others destroy young kittens, but in the wild state all presumably belong in the latter class, and the former doubtless are the result of thousands of years of domestication. An occasional male of the domestic breed is solicitous for his young, and Siamese males generally are excellent fathers while the young are immature.

Some male cats, like kittenless females, will adopt a young cat. Many examples are reported in which a male cat brought home a kitten and invited it to eat his dinner; and if a tramp cat discovers hospitality in a home he may bring other cats to share it. An interesting case of this kind is sent us by Miss Anna Nolan. A young orange Persian, Meetz, was found late one night, hungry and wet from a downpour of rain. On the third day he brought home another tramp kitten of his age, a tortoise-shell female who was named Beauty. When mature they mated, but Beauty left her crying offspring for so long a time that Meetz would get into the box and comfort them until they mistook him for their mother and tried to nurse him. Then he became indignant, cuffed them, and leapt from the box.

Many animals, including birds, maltreat one of their number if it is hurt or ill, but it has been said that the cat "possesses all the emotions of other animals and also benevolence," for if a cat is injured or sick, other cats, instead of bullying and trying to kill it, go to its rescue. We have noticed that when a tom cat was in trouble, half a dozen of his common rivals hastened to his assistance. A male cat will also befriend a female who is ill, washing her face, talking to her just as she talks to her kittens, and sleeping near by until she recovers.

The fighting and roaming instincts are so strong in the male cat that he would rather die than relinquish them. Nevertheless, cats would rather eat than fight, and a tom, be he ever so eager in the pursuit of a rival, always can be diverted by the offer of a meal.

Male cats begin to fight soon after they mature at about nine or ten months. A strong tom cat likes to show his supremacy by dominating smaller, weaker, and less combative males, and these, on seeing him approach, often try to escape; and if cats are color blind, as some laboratory experiments show, it is difficult to explain how they distinguish their enemies many feet away, unless each cat, besides having a sex odor, has its own individual odor known to others in the neighborhood. Sometimes they scream horribly before they are touched by their antagonists, who often are satisfied with this exhibition of weakness and do not pursue the argument to the point of making the fur fly. They seem to say, "You're afraid of me and that's all I wanted to know."

In fighting, the aggressor seeks to station himself in a position above his victim, if possible.

On more than one occasion we have seen a vigorous male torment a smaller one to the point of exhaustion.

Many a fine cat has met with a tragic fate because of an uncontrollable urge to roam, which comes over all male felines at one time or another in much the same manner that the urge for a change, even for the worse, possesses most human beings sooner or later. The longing for the fields and woods, where they can smell the grass and flowers and see the breezes stirring the leaves, presumably is much the same as ours, and they have the added joy of hunting grasshoppers, frogs, snakes, small mammals, and birds. In the city they roam, too, finding new cats, new smells, new places. Even after a cat has been severely injured during such excursions, he will not give them up.

NEUTER MALES

In some cases a male cat will domineer over a neuter, but often the reverse appears to be the case. A male cat of our acquaintance cuffs a much older neuter male of the same household, but a neuter cat we know chases every other cat out of his yard, including the females.

An excellent illustration is given us by Miss Verry Packard, whose Honeysuckle Pansyblossom Snowball, a neuter male, resented the roaming habits of the male cat of the household, Tommy Atkins, and when Tommy asked to be let out for his nightly excursions, Honey was always there to administer a parting cuff. "When Tommy returned next morning, ears ragged, fur torn, fagged out and ready to drop in his tracks and asking for nothing but breakfast and bed," says Miss Packard, "the schedule sometimes went off smoothly, but at other times he was obliged to take a lecture from Honey, punctuated with plenty of cuffs." Honey would sit and watch him for thirty minutes at a time, with an expression of powerful disapproval, then box his ears soundly and leave. Tommy always accepted his chastisement with a resigned meow.

Miss Linda M. French's Catiline, a neuter male, suffered from rheumatism and though able to reach a post or chair, required to be lifted down; and his temper grew uncertain with age, but his mother also had a rather uncertain temper.

A neuter cat generally will accept a kitten's introduction into the household without jealousy. Miss Lucy G. Wolfe's Spunky, a neuter male, objected to the attentions of a visiting kitten, Jubilee, who, fascinated by his plumy tail, delightedly pounced upon it. Spunky would raise one big paw as a warning, and if Jubilee did not desist, he boxed her ears. Otherwise he was very patient with the kitten, and never attempted to steal her food. He invited in a neighbor's cat, Puffy, and after romping about for awhile adjourned with her to the pantry where they opened a box of sandwich pastes and feasted on lobster spread.

One neuter cat may domineer over another neuter, just as Honey domineered over the male, Tommy Atkins. Mrs. Arthur E. Davids of Hartsdale, New York, called her coalblack pair of cats the Gold Dust Twins, and named them Goldy and Dusty. Dusty obeyed a little call which Goldy gave only for him, and was obviously repressed as long as Goldy lived. Goldy, asleep in a wicker rocker up-stairs one morning, was roused by a guttural "er-er-er" as Dusty entered the room bearing a large slice of liver. Mrs. Davids snatched the morning paper in time to "place the cloth" for Goldy's unexpected meal, which he, jumping down, accepted with an appreciative grunt, while Dusty sat solemnly watching his enjoyment, then jumped into the rocker himself for a nap. The butcher's boy had left the day's order down-stairs on the kitchen table. Disregarding a leg of lamb, Dusty helped himself to a slice of liver, then selected another for his dictator. After Goldy's death Dusty became very alert and aggressive, though never nervously active.

We are indebted to Miss Lucy G. Wolfe for an original observation on the behavior of a neuter male in the presence of mating cats. When Dotsy, a neighbor's female cat of whom Spunky was a close friend and playmate, began to "call," two tom cats responded and engaged in considerable quarreling. Spunky sat at a distance watching the fray in apparent bewilderment, and would have nothing to do with Dotsy. Miss Wolfe says, "He really seemed to be afraid of her."*

MOTHER CATS

A cat having only one kitten sometimes takes it to a nursing mother cat to be cared for, or expects her owners to rear it. This also has happened when a cat had a number of kittens. The explanation apparently is that the mother cat has no milk. When a cat kills her kittens the reason commonly assigned is eclampsia (puerperal convulsions) superinduced by pain. In some instances, however, the same cause which operates in the case of dogs and pigs that devour their young undoubtedly operates in the cat's case, *i.e.*, a lack of sufficient minerals in the diet. In one case, however (described in *The Cat Gazette* for December, 1938), a mother cat promptly destroyed an eight-legged kitten, seeming to recognize it as a monstrosity.

*Few observations have been made on the habits of spayed cats.

After the kittens are born and washed the mother cat does not leave them for twenty-four hours, during which time their intake of nourishment is constant. On the second day she permits herself a brief airing, and on the third day remains out longer. The third night she may go hunting for a field mouse and be absent for several hours. After the third day she lies in the nest box most of the day whether the kittens wish to nurse or not, and leaves them toward night for several hours or even for half the night. In cool weather she warms herself on entering the house, before approaching her young; and she gauges her leap into the nest box by looking in first to see where the kittens are. Though a faithful mother, she respects her own rights and if the kittens cry for her when she is out of the box stretching her muscles she growls angrily—but returns to them at once. If she considers conditions unfavorable for her kittens she changes their nest. One city cat, feeling that her kitten was unsafe at home, carried it over the fence and laid it at the door of a kind neighbor, returning regularly to nurse it; and it found a good home where its mother had taken it. Mr. Thomas W. Rutherford informs us that a country cat whose kittens were being disturbed by children repeatedly swam a stream twenty-five feet wide with a kitten in her mouth until she had carried them all across and established a new home on the other side where they could not be reached. This cat happened to be a habitual swimmer.

Some cats have milk for several months after bearing young. In others, particularly those inhabiting hot countries, it begins to disappear after the fourth week. As a rule the cat nurses her kittens for two months or longer, bringing them small rodents and birds when they are seven weeks old or earlier.

A cat can count and notices immediately if one of her kittens is missing. She also has favorites among her kittens.

When bereft of her young she will take back the kittens of previous litters or adopt small mammals of almost any species to relieve her distress—mice, rabbits, hedgehogs, foxes, wolves, puppies, etc. One cat carried home six little skunks from the woods, and as fast as they were returned by the game warden she carried them back. A woman destroyed all her cat's kittens and gave the cat two baby squirrels to nurse instead. She accepted them, though looking rather puzzled. One kittenless little mother was seen thrusting a half-grown cat under her to coax it to nurse, which it refused to do. She seemed to think a certain tom cat responsible for her suffering and growled at him and clawed him savagely. In rare instances a cat has drawn off her own milk, or another female cat has done this for her.

Even if a mother cat has several kittens, she sometimes adds strange young mammals to her family, such as baby rats or squirrels. Since the reason for this does not reside in a desire to have her milk drawn, it appears to be based on a simple instinct of generosity, such as that which prompts a tom cat to bring home a young friend. In the case of human infants, a mother cat has been seen to slap a baby whose persistent crying annoyed her, and she has also been seen to carry some trinket to a baby to play with. The mother cat takes playthings to her kittens and one cat, Thisbe, took little china ornaments off a dresser and put them in the basket for her young to play with. If they

The cat teaches a puppy to respect it

A mother cat sometimes adds strange young mammals to her
family, such as baby rats.

were returned to the dresser, the cat took them away again in the same manner.

If she has had no kittens, a female cat will steal a kitten (just as a chickless turkey will steal a chick).

No known animal is prouder and happier than a cat with kittens, and in the protection of her young she is unsurpassed in vigilance and courage. Tom cats are fearful of her.* In a case reported to the author a female cat very neatly castrated a male that approached her nest.

Miss Edna M. Hopkins tells us that the man of a certain household drowned the entire litter of their mother cat while his wife was at church one Sunday morning. After a time she had more kittens and was contented with them in a basket in the kitchen until she saw her mistress getting ready to go out, leaving her alone with her master. Then she suddenly became frantic and began to carry off the kittens, one by one. She placed two in a little box in an up-stairs closet, where she sat on them to hide them.

Two mother cats on friendly terms frequently pool their families, one caring for the kittens while the other absents herself, and the entire brood of a sick or dying mother will be taken over by another nursing mother with great intelligence and sympathy. In one case two cats in the same house had litters a day apart, one having four, the other seven kittens. They occupied separate drawers. When one cat left her kittens the other would get them and put them with hers. When the cat came back and found an empty drawer she understood what had happened and merely crawled

*Note how one cat, Amos, has remembered for seven years about a mother cat that frightened him, p. 131.

in and waited until the other cat went away. Then she carried all eleven kittens to her own nest. Cats with much experience in rearing kittens may give instructions to younger cats. A lady who owned two cats says that the older had stopped breeding when the younger had kittens, one of which she was permitted to keep. The old cat loved to get into the basket and cuddle the kitten. One day, before the kitten's eyes were open, the young mother decided to nurse it in the living room, upon seeing which the old cat immediately picked it up and carried it up-stairs into a dark cupboard.

Miss Edna M. Hopkins tells us that when Tommy was small his mother, Periwinkle, would carry him up-stairs away from his brothers and sisters, and his grandmother, Pussy, would go up and get him and carry him down. Many a ride he took up and down before he could walk. Tommy no doubt was his mother's favorite kitten. He has been gelded and she still is exceedingly devoted to him.

Miss Violet M. Turner informs us that a man who, with considerable heartache, asphyxiated a mother cat and her kittens in a gas retort he had made for the purpose, found later that in her effort to preserve her offspring the cat had covered the entire five with her body.

We have two instances in which a mother cat, deeply devoted to her mistress, was believed to have deferred the arrival of her kittens until her mistress was at hand.

Says Miss Anna Nolan:

Petty Zou would not give birth to her kittens until Julia (my sister, who was a teacher) returned from school. She would cry if Julia left her for a minute. My brother called Julia "the cats' midwife."

Says Mrs. Beatrice Greig:

As Pealette grew up her whole life was bound up in mine, and so when her kittens were expected I knew what was expected of me! Friends were staying with me and we were invited out to tea. Very reluctantly I agreed to go. I placed Pealette in her box prepared for the accouchement and explained to her, "I have to go out. Can you wait till I come back? I will come soon."

When I returned I dashed up to my room and there was Pealette sitting up in the box watching for me. I kissed and fondled her and began to take off my afternoon gown. No sooner was it off than she called to me and the first baby came. My friends had to dine alone. A tray came up to me, and all went well and most happily.

A mother cat has been known to compel the family dog to care for her kittens and keep them warm while she went for an airing. On the other hand, though friendly with the house dog, a mother cat may not permit him to approach her kittens, and if his curiosity gets the better of him in her absence and he is caught with the kittens, he is soundly slapped and "sworn at" when she returns.

Alleged Breeding with Unrelated Animals. Many country people believe that the female cat mates with unrelated animals, such as the lynx, raccoon, rabbit, and skunk: the lynx because of the prevalence of short-tailed cats in northern New England; the raccoon because of the long hair of the Angora (known throughout New England as the coon cat) and the raccoonlike toeing in of some Angoras, particularly noticeable in blotched tabbies whose color resembles that of the raccoon; the rabbit because of the long hind legs, stilted gait and bobbed tail of many cats (called rabbit cats, also bobtail cats) in the New England and Middle Atlantic states; and the skunk because of the friendliness sometimes exhibited by female cats for skunks.

The bobtailed condition and long hind legs result not from an ancestry embracing the lynx or the rabbit, but from Manx cat forebears, these cats showing strong Manx characteristics such as shyness toward strangers, refusal to permit strange dogs and cats on the premises, leaping proclivities, etc. The raccoon and rabbit never have been seen to mate with the cat even when the animals have been living harmoniously under the same roof. We have interviewed and corresponded with owners of mother cats known to have been close friends with skunks and alleged to have produced kittens by them. The kittens never were available (disposed of because of their skunklike odor!), but were described as having been of small size, with dorsal stripes of black and white like those of skunks, also as having turned tail, skunk fashion, when annoyed, though not emitting any fluid at such times.

There is no proof whatever that the female cat mates with any of the animals mentioned, nor with any other unrelated animals.*

*The male cat has never been involved in this curious superstition.

Chapter Fifteen

HABITS AND INSTINCTS

BOXING EARS

BOTH MALE and female cats will box a misbehaving kitten or puppy, as a bear boxes its cubs. Grown cats also cuff one another. Lions have been observed to do the same, and it is probable that boxing ears is a characteristic of felines in general, as it is of bears.

CLEANLINESS*

The domestic cat's cleanliness is proverbial. Its tongue, which in the healthy cat is free from bacteria, is applied directly to the fur, except that in washing the face, ears, and head, one of the fore paws is moistened with saliva and used as a washrag. The habit of covering its excrement has been attributed to a primitive instinct to conceal its presence from enemies and prey, but this theory is unsound, inasmuch as cats cover other things and with no such motive, and many wild felines, even those of small size, do not cover their excrement. Every one who has owned a cat has seen it cover food that was distasteful, and Darwin's grandfather noticed that a kitten scratched ashes over a spoonful of water that had been spilled on the hearth. Very intelligent cats also make use of a seat in the bathroom and with no thought of covering their scent. The kitten covers its excrement with-

*"The cat is a Brahmani, nice and clean."—Hindu saying.

185

out instruction, and we suspect that the object of this powerful instinct of cleanliness in the domestic feline is to keep its surroundings habitable for itself, *i.e.,* dry and sweet.

Cats become excited if prevented from leaving the house when they desire, and one that was shut in a room clawed a hole through the window screen in order to get out.

DELIBERATING ON THE DOOR-SILL

The cat has a habit, annoying to many people who do not understand the reason for it, of being in a vast hurry to get out and yet, when the door is opened, standing on the sill deliberating so long that it is in danger of having its tail shut in. Why does it do this? The only explanation that has been offered is that it is testing the elements with those delicate receiving instruments, its vibrissæ and the hairs of its back, which are finely attuned to the slightest vibration of air; but cats that live among rocks, as did some of the wild ancestors of the domestic cat, may have a habit of looking about carefully for enemies before leaving their dens, and the cat's habit of looking about before leaving the house may hark back to some such habit of its forebears. Even after leaving the door, the cat sometimes deliberates on the stoop for five or ten minutes before carrying into effect the errand for which it was so eager to get out. It does not deliberate on the door-sill when it wishes to enter the house, but comes in speedily.

HOMING—A SENSE OR AN INSTINCT?

The cat shares the homing "instinct" in common with limpets, mason bees, certain fishes, turtles, homing pigeons, man, and other animals. Homing has been called a "muscle sense," and it is true that the cat's muscle sense is much more delicate than that of human beings; but many persons who possess as perfect a sense of direction as any cat will not agree that it is a muscle sense. It has been proved that the homing faculty is independent of memory and the senses of sight, hearing, and smell. (See p. 147.)

All cats do not possess the homing faculty and some cannot find their way home if carried only one-tenth of a mile away. A great many removed from their homes have never returned, but the majority presumably made the attempt and met with some accident on the way. Many cats, however, can find their way home though blindfolded or anesthetized on the journey, and when taken out in a small boat have been observed to turn toward home regardless of the revolutions of the boat.

There are many authenticated instances of cats reaching home from very long distances, though some are quicker than others in finding their way back, possibly due to being obliged to spend less time escaping from enemies and procuring food. One cat returned two miles in ten hours, another three miles in seventy-eight hours, another covered ten miles in forty-eight hours, and one made forty miles in three weeks, while a fifth, that had a river to cross, covered sixty-five miles in six months; but a sixth, also crossing a river, covered seventy-three miles in four days. Herrick reported the case of a cat that covered 200 miles between Huddersfield and London in four days. One cat is said to have carried each of six kittens ten miles, making in all 110 miles, in three days.

The National Humane Review (May, 1936) printed an account of a cat named Cookie, who was sent by express from Chicago to an aunt of his owner living in Nebraska, and returned home, 600 miles. Ripley's account of the incident states that the journey was covered in six months. If a homing pigeon can return 2000 miles in three weeks,* a cat should be able to cover 600 miles in six months, though its feet are not adapted to walking as are a pigeon's wings to flight.

There is a classic story of a Belgian society which planned to train cats for carrying messages in place of carrier pigeons, but the plan never matured. In the preliminary experiments it is said that thirty-seven cats were taken twenty miles into the country from a town in Belgium in bags and set free, and that every cat reached home within twenty-four hours. Perhaps it is more remarkable when a cat returns home after more than a year's absence from a distance of only thirty miles and when she is approaching maternity. Through Mrs. Emmons White the author has received from Mr. Austin L. Kenyon of Elmira, New York, the following account: "In June, 1935, we sent our three-colored cat, Cammy, to a friend on a farm at Leona, Pennsylvania. She was crated and transported in a car about thirty miles. In July this year, 1936, she came home. A few hours after she came back she gave birth to four beautiful kittens."

Through Mrs. H. E. Leavitt of San Francisco we have the following account, sent by Mrs. Edna Buckbee:

We had a plain gray house cat that came to us as a kitten and remained for several years. It happened to be in our woodshed which was situated on the famous Angel's Creek when a cloudburst broke in the mountains. Water backed up the creek and carried away the woodshed with the cat in it, washing it down the stream forty-five miles, where it was thrown into an eddy,

*The Rural New Yorker, October 10, 1936.

and a man on the lookout for bodies or refuse coming down the stream found the cat and took it home. That night the cat left his place and a week later was in Angel's Camp. It must have walked back for it was all in, but with feeding and a good rest it became as good as ever.

Charles Platt cites the case of a cat that returned home after six years' absence and immediately sought his old resting place.

The expression "A cat has nine lives" refers not so much to its power to resist injury and disease as to its ability to outwit human effort to destroy it. When there was in the human heart less humanity toward animals than at the present time, the custom was to carry to a long distance an unwanted cat, or even to attempt to drown it, but often "The cat came back," which gave rise to still another saying, "Never was cat drowned that could see shore." We have an amazing illustration from Mrs. Harry Thomas Folger of Nashville, Tennessee, who says,

When I was a girl at home we had a mother cat that we got tired of because of the continuous families. Some friends who were driving out into the country offered to take her out with them. They left her at a farm about ten miles out in the hills (Idaho). In a few days she came back, rather the worse for wear. Then my father put her in a heavy sack with some stones, tied it with strong cord and dropped her in the main irrigation canal, which was deep, wide and swift and only a few blocks from our home. In about a week back she came, a very thin and dirty cat. I can't imagine how she could have gotten out or where she could have been all that time. She looked as though she had been through a lot.

PLAY, AND PURSUIT OF MOVING OBJECTS

A cat seldom is too old to exhibit a playful spirit. Two

grown cats will race like kittens through the house, a whirlwind of merriment, and a mother cat plays with her kittens —an unusual phenomenon in the animal kingdom. Though fond of warmth, cats love to play in the snow. It is this spirit of fun which helps to endear these animals to many lonely people.

To Mrs. Edith W. Berwyn's cat, Ginger, a nail or anything that makes a little noise when rolled on the floor is fascinating, and all her cats enjoy playing with the "light bird" reflected from a mirror. Beauty Nugent (chapter on Longevity) took jewelry off the dresser and dropped it on the floor to hear the noise, and Mickey Rendell likes to hide Mrs. Rendell's jewelry under a rug.

The cat's instinct is to pursue and play with any small moving object. Lafcadio Hearn thought its racial memory tells it which creatures are dangerous and exactly how to kill a venomous serpent; but we have records of cats which have been severely bitten by snakes, and have seen many a kitten nipped by an insect to which it applied its nose too closely. It is certain that the kitten must learn by experience with which creatures it may safely play, and after one unpleasant encounter it develops great caution.

SMILING*

The smile of the kitten is broad, purely happy, and somewhat prospective. The smile of the cat is more or less of a smirk, and comes from sheer contentment and pleased retrospection. No cat or kitten smiles except when well treated and talked to.

*"She wears the same voluptuous slow smile
  She wore when she was worshiped on the Nile."
                                    —Walter Adolphe Roberts.

THIEVING

Some cats persistently steal and others do not. No doubt the most honest will steal when starving. Of two female cats adopted when large kittens into the same home, one never could be taught not to steal, while the other pilfered nothing. The Persian went along to the refrigerator when milk or other refreshment was to be taken out for her, and if there were chicken or meat in the box she would pull it out in the twinkling of an eye. The other cat was a great ratter and supplemented her home fare with many a pound of rodent meat, so that her hunger never was so acute as that of the Persian, who found birds easier to catch and therefore had no extra food in winter.

In one case a cat was given to a neighbor with the warning that she was an incorrigible thief. In her new home she stole nothing, but it was learned that her former owner never gave her enough to eat.

A small black female cat that lived in a public aquarium and was fed beef heart and clams and fish never stole, even though the men's meat sandwiches were left uncovered, and never went fishing in the tanks. She was a valiant ratter.

When the bell rang for meals, Dillo arrived promptly from anywhere and took his rightful place at his master's left hand. When Mrs. Greig was present he was served second; when alone, first. On Sundays Mr. Greig's cold supper would be placed on the table and left, and often he would not go down for it at once, but Dillo had heard the bell and was there and was never known even to look at the cold chicken. Says Mrs. Greig, "He knew past all knowing that his drumstick was absolutely inviolate and certain."

Habitual thieving in a cat therefore appears to be due in part to its nature, in part to lack of early training, but principally to want of sufficient food.

DISCOVERING INTRICATE WAYS OF
REACHING HOME

The cat sometimes reaches home by devious ways, which can hardly have been discovered in all cases by accident, but occasionally must result from observation and reflection.

Miss E. G. Chapin of New York City describes Yankee Doodle, her brown tiger coon cat from Maine, who began to appear every few nights in her third-story front room, the door of which was closed but the window of which was open. Subsequent events proved that he traversed the back fence until he came to a cross street, where he descended to the sidewalk and went around the corner to the sixth house, which had a heavy growth of Virginia creeper on its front. His home was three houses beyond. He climbed this vine to a point where he could hop along the window sills of the third story, crossing two houses and entering his mistress' open window. The proof of his method came when he was missing for a full day and Miss Chapin heard a mournful yowl under her window. Looking out, she beheld Yankee Doodle sitting on the capstone above the second-story window, unable to get up or down. He had miscalculated and got onto the wrong level. She was able to rescue him, after securing her feet in a heavy chair for balance, by lifting him by the scruff of the neck into the window above.

This cat loved to take his naps in the crotch of a large fruit tree in the back yard, about eight or ten feet above the ground.

DISPLAYING CATCH

Most cats take home their catch for praise and admiration, and some hoard their booty by storing it under a piece of furniture such as a grand piano, where a collection of mice, grubs, grasshoppers, frogs, etc., sometimes accumulates.

Mrs. Edith W. Berwyn tells us that whenever Rowdy caught live things in the canyon or terraces "he would bring them home to show us, with a loud meow. Once he carried in a lizard so large he had to sidestep its tail dragging on the ground." The author's long-haired brown tabby often brought home snakes in the same manner.

Mrs. Beatrice Greig says, "Rufus used to bring everything he caught to me—rats, lizards, and once he brought a live mouse into my bed. When I went away everything was placed under my bed and dared not be touched, smelt it ever so high, until I returned."

The habit of taking home the catch may be a survival of an original habit of the wild animal of carrying its prey to its den to be devoured in security from the raids of other animals. An example of the fixation of this habit occurred in a kitten belonging to Mrs. Doone Burks. It had been trained always to eat from a certain dish in a certain spot. When it made its first catch it carried it into the house, laid it in the dish, and ate it there.

Once a cat has been praised for rodent catching, it will carry home everything it captures, from bugs to rabbits, for exhibition and approval.

STRANGE FOOD HABITS

Although the entire cat family is classified as carnivorous, all the smaller felines, such as lynxes, jaguarundis, ocelots, and wild cats, are omnivorous, and the natural food of the domestic cat consists of birds and rodents, small fishes, frogs and other water creatures, snakes, salamanders, lizards, insects and bugs, grass and other vegetation, from which it will be seen that its fare is largely acid-forming. Under domestication it has developed an astonishing appetite for fruits, vegetables, bakery stuffs, and queer beverages, including starchy foods and alkaline-forming solids and liquids.

Most of our very old felines (chapter on Longevity) were fond of potatoes. Most cats like succotash, macaroni, noodles, peas, parsnips, squash, bread, cake, cereals, puddings, and other starchy foods. Asparagus is believed to be the favorite vegetable of nearly all cats. They also favor cucumber, eggplant and celery, raw turnips, raw carrots, beets; and some like onions, as well as melons, nuts, coconut, raisins, lemon peel, dates, figs, olives, and grapes. One cat loves avocados with mayonnaise. We have noticed very hungry city cats that preferred mushrooms to meat. Cats like puppy biscuits and some of the prepared cat foods. They are fond of greens, lettuce, catnip, verbena, valerian, patchouli, lavender, grass, beach grass, umbrella grass (*Cyperus alternifolius*), California bluebell, and the silver vine (*Actinidia polygama*). The silver vine is eaten entire—root, branch, stem, and leaf.

Dairy products are eagerly accepted—eggs, butter, cheese, and milk in every form, including ice cream, junket, and custard. Other beverages taken are tea, coffee, tomato juice, fruit juices, broths, and alcoholic liquors. The love for milk is universal among the Felidæ, great and small, though they get it in a state of nature only in the udders of the adult and the stomachs of the young mammals on which they prey.

All kinds of cooked meat and sea food, including ham, shellfish and tripe, are enjoyed, but an occasional cat will eat no meat, raw or cooked.

The Felidæ are said not to visit the salt-licks as do birds and herbivorous animals. One theory, therefore, is that cats do not require salt; but they like salt bacon, salt butter, salt olives, salted nuts, and salt in their food, and their eyes are brighter and general health bettered when a small amount of salt is added to the diet. In a state of nature they may occasionally get salt, like milk, from the animals on which they prey.

Cats have a strange habit of nibbling from the fingers of a person they like many things for which they show an aversion if these are placed in their food dish or on the floor. Everyone who has kept cats has had one like Catiline, who wanted bits of crackers when Miss French's father munched them, but if a whole one were put on the floor he would not touch it. Miss Edith Rice of New York City owns an orange Persian, Daffodil, who dislikes ginger snaps, yet when a lady he knows called and brought him some he ate two, but refused to touch them after she left.

Some cats will not lap, but prefer to scoop up the milk in one paw and lick it off. Others will not eat from a dish, but pick up the food in one paw and eat it much the same as a person eats from the fingers.

Torrance says that in China (1926) pigs' entrails are fed after being boiled with a pinch of sulphur and the water thrown away. Kittens of eight or nine months, the Chinese believe, change their intestines, and then are given chicken guts cooked and fed whole. In parts of the Orient from time immemorial cats have been fed on rice and fresh-water fish cooked together, and very anciently they received wine. Their present odd tastes, therefore, have been developed during thousands of years of domestication in different lands by different races of men.

In devouring cheese, eggs, carrots, rice and nuts, cats may benefit by their calcium content, which corrects upsets in the organic equilibrium, and they may feel better for the potassium contained in raisins, celery, and vegetables in general. From milk they derive potassium and phosphorus, and their fondness for cereals may have something to do with the phosphorus and calcium content which some contain. They love mussels and shrimps, the former being particularly rich in iodine, and are said to eat sea-kale, which, though of the mustard family, is doubtless rich in iodine.

Whether cats know what foods are or are not beneficial is a moot question, with some evidence in the affirmative. A cat during difficult parturition will refuse milk but accept alcoholic liquors. Miss Annie A. Chadbourne informs us that her cat, Billy, was "very fond of cold potato and also of triscuits on which a tiny bit of sugar had been sprinkled and hot water poured over the triscuits to soften them, then the top of the milk added. For two years, I should say, before the end [at eighteen years] he would not touch either. I have wondered if his instinct did not tell him that such food was not good for a cat with a diabetic tendency."

THE DRAMATIC INSTINCT

The dramatic instinct in the cat is very strong. It likes games and for the love of a person consents to learn tricks, and is the only one of the Felidæ that ever enjoys their performance. Many cats teach themselves tricks, such as standing up to beg and walking backward and forward on their hind legs. If a cat does something unusual, for which it is properly complimented, it may repeat the performance indefinitely.

MISCELLANEOUS HABITS AND INSTINCTS

The cat loves to rub its head and smooth its whiskers against a person, a tree, a shrub, or post.

It licks the under surface of the rough leaves of certain plants such as foxglove, just as it licks wool, and apparently for the purpose of removing loose hairs from its tongue.

Its teeth chatter when a fly traverses the window-pane or a bird flits overhead.

The contented cat rests with fore paws folded beneath its breast.

In sleeping it curls itself into a ball in cool weather and stretches out at full length when it is warm. Sometimes it sleeps with a paw over its eyes to exclude the light.

It growls over a bone or piece of meat, but does not fight over its food, and several cats will eat amicably from the same dish.

Cats out of doors have a habit of remaining for some minutes on the spot where they have received food.

After making its toilet the cat sometimes pauses for several minutes with its tongue out.

If it has suffered an injury from a dog, it may attack every dog it sees. A Maine cat, Henri, was injured by a stray dog and developed an abdominal abscess in consequence. After that he attacked every dog he saw, and the neighbors' canines feared him.

A frightened cat lengthens its body and crawls almost on

its belly, dragging its tail. A happy cat walks high, often with tail erect.

Some cats follow the instinct of the wild and go off alone when ill or dying, but if tenderly cared for they often seek the aid of those they love.

The loose skin of the cat sometimes is twitched in wavy tremors from the middle of the back to the root of the tail, the reason for which is unknown. Colette Willy thinks it is due to the perception of faint, maddening sounds imperceptible to human ears. A slight itching may cause it, more intense itching being relieved by biting the spot.

Unworried cats, like other domestic animals including dogs and horses, lie on their backs in the morning sun and roll from side to side as though in sheer enjoyment of physical being, and some observers have concluded that this is done to exercise muscles not used in other ways and to keep the internal organs in a state of general harmony. It does not occur in the underfed cat.

Cats often select as their sleeping place a drawer or a shelf beneath a shelf, and the fondness for this overhead protection may hark back to very ancient days of living among rock crevices and in the crotches of trees in the jungle.

Many cat owners have noticed that a cat will stare fixedly at a person who is occupying its chair, and it may even chastise him. When Miss Anna Nolan's cat, Petty Zou, was about twelve years old, a special rocking chair was reserved for her in the living room. A man friend who called insisted on sitting in that chair. "Pet warned him several times," says Miss Nolan, "and then dug her claw, a single long one which she used when necessary, into his thigh."

Chapter Sixteen

FRIENDSHIPS WITH VARIOUS ANIMALS

CAT-AND-CAT FRIENDSHIPS

AMONG the most conspicuous of cat friendships other than those of some mother cats for each other and for their offspring if these are females or altered males, are friendships existing between neutered cats, either two neuter males or a neuter male and a spay. Monk Hollinshead (chapter on Longevity) and his brother were inseparable, and Brother assumed toward Monk the attitude of a body-guard, never allowing him out of his sight. Mrs. Walter L. Hamilton's cats, Heidie, a neuter male, and Mina, a spay, loved each other dearly and often were seen asleep locked in each other's embrace. Heidie was a great ratter and mouser, and Mina sat at table with the family, always with perfect manners and waiting patiently to be served.

Mrs. Margery Bianco informs us that a cat, Happy, was sitting on a beam in the woodshed when a strange dog, a collie, chased another cat into the shed. Happy dropped instantly onto the collie's back and clung there with her claws until he yelped and ran away. The rescued cat was a companion of Happy's.

Instances have occurred in which a cat, having brought home a guest to sample his dinner, accepted a similar invitation from the guest. Many more cases are on record in which a cat brought home a hungry friend, and in one instance as more food was piled on the plate, more and more guests were invited to partake of it.

A blue cat, Dicky Purdum, well known to the author, often met a yellow cat that lived in the woods near by and escorted him across a railroad track down to the shallows, where he deftly fished out minnows for his homeless friend to eat.

Wood's cat, Pret, disapproving of meat left by the cat's meat man for another cat, carried it to the cellar and buried it under a heap of coal, and then took his own dinner to his friend.

A tom cat observed by the author became strongly attached to a female cat belonging in the neighborhood, visiting her daily and washing her face, though she sometimes slapped him for his trouble. When she failed to show a proper appreciation of his attentions, he wound up by slapping her, so that this friendship, though constant, was somewhat hectic.

CAT-AND-DOG FRIENDSHIPS

Some remarkable cat-and-dog friendships exist, and if properly trained most dogs get along amicably with cats. Dogs owned by the fire departments in some of the larger cities now are trained to rescue cats from burning buildings. Cats and dogs sometimes go off hunting together, or hunting with people, and Hudson tells of a black cat that accompanied a pack of hounds and at the first shot dashed off before the dogs to retrieve the bird.

A fox terrier, Roxy, and a tom cat, Teddy, the pets of

CAT–AND–DOG FRIENDSHIP

Roxy, fox terrier, and Teddy, tom cat, belonging to Mr. and Mrs. Oscar Dewey of Holyoke, Mass., were so deeply attached to each other that when the cat sustained an injury to his head the dog attended the wound every day with his tongue until it healed.

Chappie the Globe Trotter traveled for two years in Europe and the Orient with his owner, Miss Alice Engel of New York City. His double front paws helped to win him distinctive courtesies.

Mr. and Mrs. Oscar Dewey of Holyoke, Massachusetts, were so fond of each other that when the cat sustained an injury to his head the dog tended the wound every day with his tongue until it healed. Robert Cochrane records a case in which a dog extracted a needle from the neck of a cat he loved.*

Keno, says Miss Isa A. De Pledge, feels a strong responsibility for the cats, and if they wish to come in the house he makes a great fuss until some one opens the door for them.

Amos, says Mrs. Rosenberger, and Polly the dog, travel about in the family car and have covered thousands of miles. When Polly gets out, Amos wants to go too. The two animals walk together on leashes on sidewalks, along roadsides, through woods, on a boardwalk, and on the sand at the seashore.

The following story, sent us by Mr. Frank Mellen, is told by Police Sergeant Lloyd C. Slade of Rockville Centre, New York:

Our dog, half police and half wolf, is gentle and playful. Our cat is large and of a happy disposition. The two animals dwell in harmony which becomes more firmly cemented after occasional spats. A trespassing chow dog one day flew at my dog and attacked him. Surprised, and with no fighting experience, the young dog was outclassed. He whined and turned over on his back and tried to ward off the aggressor with his paws. I started to aid the under dog and was overtaken by a gray streak which flashed past and landed on the chow's back. Fastening his claws in the dog's ears, the cat bit away at his neck. The battle ended in his immediate retreat, while the cat jumped off his back, and looking

*Four Hundred Animal Stories, VI, Cat Stories (1897?)

critically at his dog companion, administered a smart cuffing on general principles. Then life moved on as before.*

In a case widely noted in the press during 1939, a long-haired white-and-gray cat, Fluffy, and a mongrel dog, Buddy (part collie, part police), had become such warm friends over a number of years in the home of Mr. and Mrs. George E. Blomquist of Cambridge, Massachusetts, that when the dog was taken to a hospital for an operation, the cat refused food for a week. She then was taken to the hospital to visit her canine friend, and after a touching reunion was able to eat again, and her presence also exerted a beneficial influence on the dog. (Mrs. Blomquist has kindly verified these facts.)

CAT-AND-HORSE (ALSO PIG) FRIENDSHIPS

Many cats love horses with a deeper love than that arising from a mere sensuous enjoyment of the warmth of their backs, though this has been sufficiently strong to cause a horse that loved a cat to sleep standing to accommodate its little friend. Cats have died of grief over the death of a loved horse.

They also become greatly devoted to pigs, sometimes sitting on their backs as they do on the backs of horses and possibly for the same reason. W. H. Larrabee relates the story of a cat that spent her time in the constant company of a pig, and when the pig was slaughtered she remained beside his body all night, and her grief was pitiful to see.†

*This cat, Skippy, later carried home a neighbor's kitten which its owner had left for dead after it was struck by an automobile the night before, and led his owners to the injured animal. A veterinarian who was summoned treated the kitten and it recovered.

†"Cats and Their Friendships," *Popular Science Monthly,* May, 1890, p. 91.

CAT-AND-REPTILE FRIENDSHIPS

Cats and turtles, and cats and alligators, many times have established very friendly relations. Sarah E. Trueblood mentions a cat, Christopher Columbus, who was a terrible fighter and keen in asserting his rights, but who would allow a turtle he had befriended to take the tenderest bone from between his jaws. Captain Hastings Mahony tells us that his two cats, Ben Turpin and Dolly, and the two turtles eat from the same platter. Mr. Thomas W. Rutherford says, "We brought from Florida an alligator about one and one-half feet long, and for over a year a kitten we had was his inseparable companion—played with him and slept with him."

CAT-AND-RODENT (ALSO FISH) FRIENDSHIPS

Cats develop affections for rodents and will protect them from enemies. Singularly enough, if a cat is friendly toward a mouse or rabbit, this does not prevent it from discriminating between the friend and others, and it will go out and prey on the same species of animals which it finds wild, or capture them and take them home to display. The same applies to fishes. Captain Mahony says that Ben Turpin goes out to fish in the river, but at home he plays with the Channa (a Chinese walking fish) by poking his paw in the water in a tantalizing way, though never hurting the fish.

Cats have become devoted to mice, rats, rabbits, squirrels, and other rodents. Nor are white rats the only ones with which they form companionships. Hudson tells of a cat that was friendly toward a common gray rat until the rat pulled out too much of her fur to line its nest, when she drove it from the house and it never returned. Friendly cats and rabbits will eat from the same dish, and the cat may be seen munching cabbage while the rabbit chews a chunk of liver.

CAT-AND-BIRD FRIENDSHIPS

Innumerable instances have been recorded in which cats of both sexes have sheltered a brood of chicks or ducklings, and even wild felines will befriend birds on occasion. In a recent instance an American bobcat (lynx) in captivity was offered a white hen for its dinner but refused to eat the bird and they became fast friends. We learn also of an Ohio Manx cat that would not touch a white chicken, but considered black Minorcas fair game.

Many cats that have become attached to birds kept in the same household enter the aviary room at night without disturbing the birds. Those who have kept an aviary know that if a mouse enters the room at night every bird leaves its perch and clings nervously to the highest wire until morning. Perhaps the cats in such cases keep the room free from the mice the birds so greatly fear.

Cats that are friendly toward their owner's chickens will drive other cats, also foxes, off the premises; but they will drive away or kill a neighbor's chickens, knowing instantly which ones are strangers. Among numerous examples, we have selected the following to illustrate this singular behavior of the cat:

Says Miss Sarah Hurd, "Tiger was kept busy in summer chasing the neighbors' hens home. How he picked them out from ours was a puzzle to them and to us."

Says Miss Verry Packard:

To give you the "bad" side of Honeysuckle I must include the story of our two hens, Mandy Lea and Becky Sharp. Mandy was an excellent mother, but Becky just couldn't be bothered with them after they had been hatched, and Mandy had to take over Becky's families. Each had her favorite rooster, Mandy's choice being Buster Brown and Becky's Dinkelspiel. When Mandy had collected all the chicks, Buster would settle on the ground, spread his wings, and dig his beak into the soft earth until Mandy and her brood came to him. The chicks would cuddle under his wings for hours while Mandy rested or took a stroll, and after this all the neighbors' chicks would climb over him.

Honey would crouch in the grass, watch the chicks, and when they came close he would kill them if they belonged to others than those of Mandy's or Becky's brood—kill them instantly and pay no more attention to them.

Brother was mortified every time it happened. He would say, "If Honey would just for once kill one of ours!" But he didn't. Tommy Atkins, on the other hand, did not seem to see the chickens.

Mrs. Floyd Van Liew of Atchison, Kansas, has a long-haired cat, Wampus, who aids her in corraling fledglings that fall from their nest. Says Mrs. Van Liew:

It would be a great thing if all cat owners would teach their cats to refrain from catching birds, and it can be done with a little patience and understanding. . . .

I never allowed the mother of Wampus to catch birds, but she never went to any trouble to protect them as Wampus does. I have always taken in fledgling birds and raised them until they could fly, then turned them out. One robin has decided it doesn't want to go out at all and sits for hours in the kitchen window mocking the birds outside. Wampus stays down in the basement with it and sometimes when I open the basement door for him to come up he will mew and refuse to come unless I get Tom, his robin, and bring it up too.

Last spring when I was training the honeysuckle with Wampus near by watching me, the jays were making a lot of noise under some near-by trees. Suddenly the cat gave a start and rushed over beneath the trees, where he picked up a wren, took it into the kitchen and laid it gently by the box in which I had two small robins, looking at me inquiringly. It gasped a few times and was dead. The blue jays had killed it.

Once Wampus circled around a huge toad, just as he circles around a fledgling until I go and get it, and he acted very disappointed because I did not bring in the toad he had found.

Miss Carrie A. Bissell of Westwood, New Jersey, sends us the following remarkable incident: A cat named Hobson was friendly toward the canary of the house which often was allowed its freedom and had even flown out of doors on one occasion and returned to its cage of its own free will. It flew out of doors a second time and failed to return. Hobson was a great mouser and often took his captures to his mistress, Mrs. Hepburn, talking with his mouth full to attract her attention. After Mrs. Hepburn had despaired of seeing her canary again, Hobson came in, talking as usual. Thinking that he must have caught another mouse, she praised him without looking up for a time, but he insisted on attention and finally received it. He then released from his mouth the canary, unharmed.

Ben Turpin frolics with Polly, the parrot, all about the floor, and they chase each other, though neither ever attempts to injure the other.

MISCELLANEOUS GROUP FRIENDSHIPS

Animal lovers in various countries have succeeded in establishing friendships between groups of creatures not commonly associated, such as cats, birds, and rodents. Over a century ago W. Bingley, the naturalist, while stopping at an inn in Germany witnessed a strange sight. The landlord

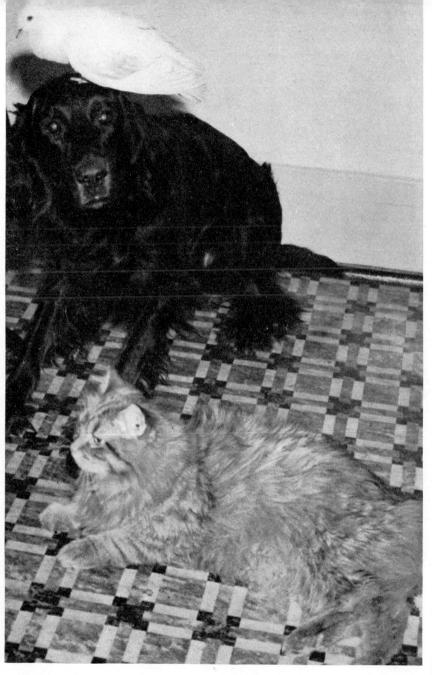

Happy family owned by Mr. and Mrs. Harry E. LaVier of Syracuse,
N. Y. Snowy, the dove, is twelve; Prince, the Gordon setter,
seven, and Goldie, the Persian cat, three years old.

Cat mummy.

placed a large dish of soup on the floor and gave a loud whistle. In came an Angora cat, a mastiff, a remarkably large rat with a bell on its neck, and an old raven. All ate from the dish, none disturbing the others, and then they all lay down except the raven, which hopped about the room. The landlord declared that the rat was the most useful, for the noise it made completely freed the house of rats and mice.

In 1850 a celebrated "Happy Family" was imported from Europe by P. T. Barnum for his American Museum. It consisted of many animals, said to have numbered between two hundred and three hundred, including cats, dogs, rabbits, guinea pigs, rats, mice, squirrels, blackbirds, pigeons, monkeys, and other birds and animals which had been trained in the "Law of Love." The rats played with the whiskers of the cats and danced on their backs, the mice nestled in the feathers of the owls, a hawk and dove "indulged in tender endearments," monkeys and birds enjoyed the same swing; and the wonderful sight was regarded as a "practical foreshadowing of the millennium," when the lion and the lamb shall lie down together. (Quoted from a contemporary account.)

Champfleury (1885) tells of a Parisian woman who "brought a cat, dog, mouse, and sparrow to live together, sleeping in the same bed and eating off the same plate." The dog, he says, "always helped himself first and amply," but left a little for the cat, who shared hers with the others.

Miss Phyllis A. Bowne says that when she was a girl the family owned a cat and a tame crow which were great friends and ate from the same dish, sometimes sharing it with a dog.

In the home of Mr. and Mrs. Harry E. LaVier of Syracuse,

New York, a firm attachment exists between a yellow Persian cat, a Gordon setter, and a white dove. The cat, Goldie, is three years old and weighs fifteen pounds, the dog, Prince, is seven, and the dove, Snowy, twelve. They live harmoniously indoors and out, in Syracuse during the winter and at Otisco Lake in summer.

Mrs. Joseph Watson of Yalesville, Connecticut, has trained various animals which are natural enemies to live peacefully together, and in her home the phrases "the fox and the goose" and "the cat and the canary" take on new meaning. Other members of her troupe are dogs, rats, mice, squirrels, rabbits, goats, lambs, and a pony, and birds such as crows, starlings, roosters, sparrow hawks, and parrots. Her happy family often has been pictured in the press and shown on the motion-picture screen.

PART FOUR

THE CAT'S EFFECT ON PEOPLE

Worship
Utilization
Fear
Hate
Love

Chapter Seventeen

ANCIENT WORSHIP OF THE CAT

A KNOWLEDGE of the cat's evolutionary rank, its remarkable physiology, psychology, and behavior, leads naturally to the question, What part has this extraordinary animal played in the general social and economic history of the human race?

It is safe to assert that no other creature in the entire zoological kingdom ever bred such depths of love and hate in the human breast, and none has exemplified in like manner the truism that history repeats itself.

Before the dawn of civilization the animal undoubtedly was feared, as are wild cats today; with the advent of an organized though crude society it was sedulously courted and tamed; and finally, under an advanced civilization, it arrived at an exalted estate.

After its worship in Egypt had died out, the cycle began again in other places. It was feared and hated, then courted and utilized, and finally looms large today as an object of admiration, not to say respect, that thousands are striving to understand. It is the last creature in the world that could be characterized as superficial or unintelligent, and, supposing its brain to have been as highly developed in the days of the Pharaohs as it is today, the fact that the ancient Egyptians comprehended it perfectly furnishes a striking illustration of their intellectual attainments.

We have already glimpsed the terror and superstition inspired in some countries by this mysterious and self-sufficient creature, its taming in the prehistoric past, and the harmonious relations in which it has lived with man and other unrelated animals. We have considered it as an animal and as a personality. Now let us consider it as a god.

When twenty mighty cities lined the banks of the Nile and the art, learning, wealth, and power of the world were centered in Egypt, her entire population of 8,000,000 souls worshiped the cat. Many other Egyptian animals also were sacred—the lion, bull, jackal, wolf, dog, ram, sea fish, river fish, serpent, crocodile, lizard, certain amphibians and insects, and such birds as the hawk and ibis—about forty-two species in all.

As yet the exact reason for this animal worship is not known, but social, economic, astronomical, and other interesting theories have been advanced.

Doctor A. Buchanan, who was in Egypt in 1908, thought the Egyptians worshiped cats in recognition of their sanitary uses, and an earlier traveler, Joseph P. Thompson, entertained somewhat similar views, but said (in 1854) that it was partly for sanitary reasons and partly with a view of preserving their species that various animals and plants were set apart as sacred. The sacred plants included the onion and the leek, and if Thompson were correct, the fact that all these animals and plants still exist is somewhat embarrassing for Occidentals who, many centuries later, have only just begun to realize the importance of preserving any species, zoological or botanical.

Jean Henri Fabre also suggested a utilitarian basis for the great cat worship of Egypt and thought the Egyptians, remembering the miseries from which the domestic animals had freed them, showed their gratitude by paying honors to the cat, ox, etc.

Since Egypt was the granary of the world, the little animal which preserved its huge stores of grain from the devastation of rodents naturally was highly prized, but this does not explain its sacred character.

Some scholars declare it was worshiped solely for its beauty, while occultists insist that the Egyptians recognized its magical properties and held them in awe and reverence.

That all the sacred animals of Egypt represented totems of ancient clans or small tribes which were gradually welded by war into a nation of many tribes, each having its own totem, is a theory presented by W. M. Conway, who held that the unusual reverence paid the cat must have been due to the fact that the tribe which had this animal for its totem became the head of Egypt. The crocodile, for example, was worshiped in one place and killed in others; but the cat was sacred everywhere, although in some parts of the country cat temples and cat necropolises attested to a more concentrated worship.

Very early indeed the cat became a totem venerated all along the Nile, and Conway was convinced that a prehistoric Cat Clan, dating as far back as 4000 to 10,000 B.C., had founded Bubastis, the City of Pasht, an important center of cat worship. (This is the Pi-Beseth of the Bible, now marked by the ruins of Tell-Basta.) If out of the totems gods evolved, then out of the cat totem came Pasht, Lady of Love (or Bastet, Lady of Bubastis), who also represented the sun and the moon.*

An astronomical theory offered by George St. Clair is that the cat was an intercalary month added in the one hundred and twentieth year to rectify the calendar, the Egyptians having had three hundred and sixty-five days in the year and no leap year, and the odd six hours of the year making just a month in the one hundred and twentieth year.† This odd idea finds some support in the fact that the sacred bull, Apis, the only other animal regarded with a veneration equal to that accorded the cat, was an astronomical symbol and it was not permitted to live for more than twenty-five years, whereas the Egyptians never killed a cat. Any one who did so, even accidentally, was torn to pieces by a mob, and the dismay of an honest man who came upon a dead cat was so great that he stood at a distance, calling out in a loud voice, beating his breast and protesting his innocence.

It is not difficult to imagine that the small feline might have represented the moon because of its nocturnal habits, the dilation and contraction of its pupils, and the glistening of its eyes in semi-darkness; and especially so because the Egyptians are said to have called the cat's glowing orbs mirrors of the sun's rays which overcame the darkness of night as does the moon. It is certain that the very ancient worship of the sun embraced the cat, which was also glorified in the Temple of the Sun at Heliopolis (the Biblical On), a seat of Egyptian learning, and that a "Great Cat" was connected with the sacred persea tree which marked

*According to the *Cambridge Natural History* the word *Puss* is from Pasht. Like the word *cat*, it is found in many languages.
†"The Cat and the Moon," *Gentleman's Magazine*, 1901, v. 290. p. 251.

Pasht (Bast or Bastet), the Egyptian cat goddess, with a brood of sacred kittens. Here she is represented in human form with the head of a cat, holding in one hand a musical instrument, the sistrum, and in the other a shield bearing a cat's head.

the place of sunrise at the height of summer. Perhaps it is not irreverent to suggest that as the cat's round face and blazing orbs reminded the Egyptians of the sun, its whiskers may have reminded them of the sun's rays.

Some who contend that the cat was a sacred astronomical symbol offer in evidence the *Book of the Dead,* which explains that the male cat is the chief god, Rā himself, who was also the sun and took the form of a cat at will, Rā and cat therefore being interchangeable terms. In the Hall of Two Truths the cat is called a "Sayer of Great Words," *i.e.,* a god speaking. Some of the temple statues of Isis, chief goddess of Egypt, portrayed her with a cat's ears, and the cat goddess, Pasht, carried a sistrum, the musical rattle used in the worship of Isis. If, therefore, the cat symbolized both the chief god and the sun, and particularly if, as the distinguished Egyptologist, E. A. Wallis Budge, thought, the cat-headed Pasht was the personification of the soul of Isis, no further explanation is needed concerning the profound nature of cat worship among the Egyptians.

Up to about 2000 B.C. the cat goddess was rivaled by Sekhet (or Sakhmet), the lioness-headed goddess of war and the legendary destroyer of mankind; but between this time and 1800 B.C. the worship of Sekhet receded while that of Pasht advanced.

Pasht (or Bast or Bastet) was fashioned most frequently in bronze, in human form with the head of a cat, robed in long garments and holding in one hand a sistrum, in the other a shield, sometimes with a basket over her arm. She is depicted with long ears, also with short ears, and in some figures wears a short skirt which reveals human limbs with the feet and tail of a cat. In others she appears wholly as a cat.

The feeding of the bulls, cats, and other sacred creatures evolved upon men and women whose proud office entitled them to receive obeisance; and for the feeding of the sacred cats we read that three species of *Silurus* from the river Nile were maintained in reservoirs. The books do not state whether the Siluridæ (catfishes) were reserved for the sacred cats because of their whiskers, but it is not impossible that a whiskered fish may have seemed to the Egyptians Rā's own choice of sustenance for the Great Cat!

Pasht is named in the Pyramid Texts, and the worship of her small prototype reached its zenith about 1500 B.C., in the time of Thotmes IV, when the city of Bubastis, consecrated to the worship of the cat, was visited yearly by many zealous pilgrims from all parts of the country. John Gardner Wilkinson says that 700,000 people journeyed thither during the course of a single season, arriving in April or May by water to celebrate the great festival of Bubastis.

Men and women carried musical instruments, and considerable noise and excitement, and probably some intoxication other than religious marked these ceremonies, for, as an ancient account has it, there was "greater effusion of grape wine than in all the year besides." Cat amulets were worn, also rings, necklaces of ivory cat beads and other ornaments, some with the figure of a cat with kittens finely wrought in gems that differ with the period—calcite, lapis lazuli, red carnelian, amethyst and others; and vows and offerings were made to large figures of cats fashioned of bronze and wood, the hair of the body inlaid with gold.

Neville Langton describes small cat figures in his rare collection which are wearing collars, earrings, and necklaces, some having scarabs on their heads. (See Bibliography.) The love of perching on posts was not forgotten in these images, nor the stateliness of the animal, which is also shown in the form of a sphinx, symbolizing royal dignity. Mr. Langton states that in the British Museum a small amulet shows a sphinx guarding its kitten in true cat fashion.

In vases of glazed faience and terra cotta, and in ebony furniture, also, the sacred cat was immortalized.

THE CAT EMBALMED

The Egyptians practised embalming because of their belief in immortality, a doctrine which they originated and which has been copied by all succeeding religions in the manner in which Egyptian learning has been imitated throughout the world and Egyptian art stolen by innumerable vandals. They embalmed the great among men and the loved and sacred among animals, that the souls might one day return to the bodies and revive them; and the Egyptian embalmer used as his trademark the figure of a scarab, the sacred beetle dedicated to Rā. What might have been their thoughts could they have foreseen their cherished kings and queens and bulls and pet gazelles and cats reposing in the galleries of the great museums of the present day, some in a hemisphere whose existence was undreamed of when Egypt controlled the learning and the commerce of the world, is not pleasant to conjecture.

After four thousand years the mummies of their sacred cats have been unearthed, preserved with aromatic bitumen, oil of cedar and spices, and swathed in fine linen, some lying in sweet-scented wooden chests painted white or green and ornamented with gildings, paintings and inscriptions, these chests having been arranged on shelves in the niches of sepulchral chambers excavated to a great depth in solid rock. In some cemeteries the coffins are cat-shaped with eyes of obsidian, rock crystal, or colored paste, and in one tomb the cats were found folded in red and white linen, their heads covered with linen masks of cats. Neville Langton states that at Abydos one cruciform tomb held the remains of seventeen cats with numerous little saucers of milk. Whether the owner were rich or poor, the body of his cat was carefully embalmed and most often wrapped in linen and plaited ribbons. The rich man's cat sometimes was given a painted or gilt face, and its ears were pricked up. Majestic felines, such as those of temples and palaces, were elegantly preserved in bronze caskets with bronze statues of themselves on top, or rested in bronze boxes shaped like themselves and welded in the center.

On the death of a cat the members of the household which it had honored with its presence cut off their eyebrows as a token of affliction and all provisions contained in the house became unlawful. The little body was wrapped in cloth and carried to the embalmer's, followed by a procession of men and women who beat their breasts in token of sorrow; and solemn ceremonies accompanied the embalming of the animal, which was also buried with great pomp.

Funerals of cats are believed to have been of the second grade, costing about $300. (First-grade funerals cost about $1200 and a third-grade funeral was much cheaper.)

The cat has been found embalmed at Thebes, and cat cemeteries have been uncovered at such centers of Egyptian cat worship as Bubastis, Sakkarah, Zagazig, and Beni-Hassan, where enormous numbers of mummies have been brought to light. The pomp and ceremony with which they were interred were conspicuously absent at their exhumation. Egyptian children ran about with the mummies, batting one another with them and making the dead dust fly. At Bubastis the cemetery yielded several hundred thousand mummies, and newspapers of 1895, including *St. James's Gazette,* carried accounts of the unearthing of nearly twenty tons of mummies at Beni-Hassan, comprising the remains of one hundred and eighty thousand cats, which were despatched in shiploads to Liverpool, where they were knocked down for fertilizer at $18.43 a ton, the auctioneer using the body of an embalmed cat for his gavel.

THE CAT CULT ENDS (AS IT MAY HAVE BEGUN) IN CAT CLANS

The downfall of cat worship in Egypt did not immediately obliterate it from the earth. Like a flickering flame that dies hard and becomes fainter and fainter in dying, it appeared elsewhere in varying forms. In some countries the cat had already been treasured for centuries. In India this was evidenced by the imposition of a heavy penalty on any one who harmed the animal. In China sacrificial rites, accompanied by theatrical ceremonies, were performed in honor of the cat god during the Hsia, Shang, and Chou dynasties, 2205–225 B.C., but the *Book of Rites* is said to describe these rites as having been rendered to both the cat god and tiger god, because of their services to man, the one taking the rodents, the other the wild pigs which devoured the field crops. (It is possible that the cat god represented a wild cat, though China knew the tame cat during this period.) In Japan, in the sixth century, the services of the domestic cat in the temples where the papyrus rolls were stored earned it the honorable title of "The Guardian of the Manuscripts," and it is said that sacrifices were made to it.

Many ancient and modern soldiers have carried on their banners the image of a cat, tame or wild, and Cat Clans, the last remnants of the ancient worship of the cat on the banks of the Nile, sprang up in Teutonic, Celtic, and other countries. A cat was emblazoned on the shields and flags of Roman soldiers about 100 B.C. The crest of the Hessian tribe of Catti was a brindled cat, and the same proud device, according to K. C. McIntosh,* was adopted by the Cattani of North Britain. The ancient Burgundians, it is said, also bore the figure of a cat on their banners.

To the best of our knowledge the last remaining Cat Clan exists in the Highlands of Scotland. It rendered distinguished services during the World War. Known as the Clan Chattan, it consists not of one clan but of a confederation of about seventeen clans, and was formed in the middle of the twelfth century for the purpose of settling disputes among the individual clans and for protection against the Campbells and other large lowland clans. Several of its individual clans or septs, Macbean, Macpherson, MacGillivray, and Mackintosh, carry on their crest the motto, "Touch not the cat bot a glove" (*bot* being an old Scotch word for *without*), and the wild cat or cat-a-mountain, already described in this book as *Felis sylvestris grampia,* an animal commonly met with in the area covered by these clans and an important ancestor of our western domestic cats, is figured on the crest, sejant except in the case of the Mackintosh Clan, whose crest shows a pair rampant, the cat on the crest

*"I Sing of Cats," *North American Review,* Oct., 1928, p. 445.

symbolizing courage and liberty. The Macpherson Clan uses the battle cry, "The Black Craig of the Clan Chattan!" In the Clan Chattan each clan has its own chief, besides which there is a chief of the confederacy of clans who is called "The Captain." (Statements sometimes met with to the effect that the members of this clan are known as "The People of the Cat" and the chief of the clan as "The Great Wild Cat," are erroneous.)*

The collar badge of the Gordon Highlanders is also in the form of a wild cat.

Many European business houses selected the figure of a cat as a trademark, to advertise themselves as careful and efficient, and the image of this animal has been much used in heraldry to signify independence and freedom from all restraint. Statues of Liberty with a cat at her feet have been found in England and in Rome.

One of the most singular of martial superstitions concerned people whose features bore a real or fancied resemblance to those of a cat. They were considered supreme in bravery, strategy, and the determination to win; and it is recorded that a prediction once was made to a Persian king to the effect that he would triumph in war if his armies were commanded by a cat-faced man. Such a man was found, and "victory perched upon his banners."

In the present day this superstition appears to have narrowed down to the belief that luck attends the presence of a cat, or even the laying of the hand upon a cat. When Miss

*For information concerning the Clan Chattan we are indebted to Doctor Angus MacGillivray of Dundee, Chief of the MacGillivray Clan, and also to a rare little book loaned us by Mr. William Henry, *The Scottish Tartans, with the Badges, Arms, Slogans, etc., of the Clans.*

Alice Engel traveled with her cat, Chappie, from New York through the Mediterranean to Trieste, an able-bodied seaman early in the voyage requested permission to touch the cat—"for luck," and this being granted, all the sailors came in a procession to lay a finger on the animal.

FREYJA, THE NORSE CAT GODDESS

The cat is conspicuously present in Norse mythology, remote though that seems from Egypt and the Mediter-

From Das Buch der Katzen, by Gustav Michel

FREYJA, THE NORSE CAT GODDESS

Her chariot was drawn by two cats. Norse maidens were married on Freyja's day (Friday) if possible, and if the sun shone during the ceremony it was said of them that they had taken good care of the cat and fed her well.

ranean; and there we find Freyja, a goddess of love like Pasht, riding forth from her mansion in a car drawn by two cats, which symbolize enjoyment of the senses. Sometimes she saddles her golden boar, but on occasions of state the cats draw her chariot, as when she drives in the great funeral procession of Balder, god of the summer sunlight, who was slain by Hoder.

Freyja resembles a cat in that she lends a favorable ear to those who sue her for assistance, she is a goddess, and has flaming eyes:

> Why are Freyja's
> Eyes so sharp?
> From her eyes it seems
> That fire doth burn.*

She is beautiful, graceful, and modest like a cat, and, strangely enough, Friday was named for her, a day which in the course of time was to become of gustatory significance to many Christian pussies.

While to the Egyptians the cat goddess, Pasht, symbolized both sun and moon, we find that to the early Norsemen Freyja was of equal value with both sun and moon, a forest giant having offered to build a safe abode for the gods within the space of a single winter, provided they would give him the goddess Freyja, together with the sun and moon; but he was defeated.

Not the least significant feature of this myth of Freyja is that the early Norsemen knew the tamed cat.

Maidens of later years were married, if possible, on Freyja's day, and if the sun shone during the ceremony it was said that the bride had taken good care of the cat and fed her well.

*Lay of Thrym in the *Elder Edda*.

Chapter Eighteen

UTILIZATION OF THE CAT,
EAST AND WEST

THE NATURAL instincts of the cat, tame or wild, have given it the universal reputation of a useful animal. Very early, as history attests, these instincts placed it in the rôle of man's ally in the destruction of rodents which devour his food supplies, and of birds which strip his trees of fruit and his vines of legumes, grapes and berries. Such is the animal's value in husbandry that in the absence of a cat a farmer once made a cat scarecrow of maltese-colored flannel, which served to protect his valuable grapevines from feathered pests.

Though other pets—canaries, parrots, guinea pigs, rabbits, marmosets, goldfishes, many dogs—are not expected to be of service, the cat often is required to earn its living, and this it does in a multiplicity of ways. Even the Egyptians, who worshiped the animal and provided for it with great tenderness, utilized it not only in protecting the grain from rodents, but, as we have seen, in bird-hunting. They are believed to have used more than one species of cat, however, in retrieving birds and small game and also in the sport-hunting of apes, which were not killed but merely driven into the trees; and according to some authorities kings in other lands employed hunting cats which were not cheetas but wild cats.

Cats do not kill insects rapidly enough to be of service during grasshopper plagues, but in the ordinary course of events they protect the home against serpents and scorpions. It is said that on occasion they have been used in snake-hunting.* It has even been asserted that St. Patrick was a cat (!)

A scorpion is dispatched by first turning it on its back with a blow of the claws and holding it in position while the tail is torn off and it thus is rendered harmless, after which the remainder is eaten at leisure.

In America the cat has been utilized in bird-hunting, though not, as in Egypt, in hunting food birds. Helen Hunt Jackson tells of the hunting of linnets in California with cats, these birds being extremely destructive of fruit crops—cherries, peaches, apricots, etc. After starting the birds from the trees to enable the farmer to shoot them, the cats caught them as they fell.†

A cat hunting for itself frequently is adversely criticized, but no complaint is ever forthcoming when it goes hunting for its master. Gordon Stables, an English cat lover of a generation ago, amusingly says, "With all due respect for the game laws, I do like to see a cat come trotting home in the gloaming with a nice young leveret or a plump partridge in her mouth. Nobody is any the poorer and her master has something nice for supper."

A cat that was saved from drowning some years ago by a man who took it aboard his sloop in Long Island Sound

---

*Rengger observed that the house cat in Paraguay would battle for an hour with a rattlesnake, which it killed but never ate; but a long-haired brown tabby belonging to the author devoured her non-venomous prey, beginning with the head.

†*The Hunter Cats of Connorloa*, 1879.

Photograph by Walter L. Hamilton

The mouser has proved a valuable ally of civilized man.

From "Researches into Chinese Superstition," by Henry Doré

Fairy Cats, says the Chinese inscription, protect the mulberry
blossoms and the five crops. The flowers symbolize good
luck and preserve the silkworms from epidemics.

and later established it in his home, regularly brought the family fish from the bay and wild game from the woods.

In olden times the utilitarian value of the cat was so great that when a man and wife separated, their goods and chattels were evenly divided except that he took the cat if there was only one.

THE DESTRUCTION OF RODENTS

In recent years a window display of silk manufacture in New York was spoiled by mice which demolished the cocoons, and in Oriental silkworm breeding establishments rats and mice always have constituted a serious menace to the industry, exemplified in an old saying, "The Chinese hate rats as they hate thieves." The cocoons are opened by these rodents with their teeth and claws to extract the pupæ, of which they are very fond, alive or dead; and in the early days of silk culture in China, silkworm breeders naturally found their salvation in cats, which proved so efficacious in keeping rodents away that superstitious Chinese began to believe that even the picture or clay image of a cat would frighten them off, and such representations were called "Fairy Cats." Modern means now are employed to combat rats and mice in Chinese filatures, though cats still are kept. They are used also in protecting the native farmers from the ravages of rodents which, as a Chinese poem says, "take their toll of the five chief crops—rice, millet, wheat, hemp, bean."

The Roman agriculturist, Palladius, who flourished in the fourth or fifth century, is said to have recommended that cats be kept in artichoke gardens for protection against mice and moles, in place of weasels which previously had served this purpose.*

Darwin's classic statement that the cat's protection of the humble-bees from field mice which destroy their nests is responsible for the continued existence of heartsease and red clover, is familiar to every one.

The best feline mousers, it is believed, are those which begin mousing when very young. Generally they appear to be cats that prefer rodents to birds. A small black well-fed museum cat caught rats nearly as large as herself, but although the trees outside were inhabited by English sparrows, she never caught a bird except when beginning to wean her kittens, and then never failed to bring them one dead sparrow. City cats do not always eat their prey, and there is a prejudice against permitting them to consume rodents, but in the country one often sees a farm cat devouring a large rat, and as she does so rolling back its skin in a very neat fashion. To the farmer there is no better friend than a cat. Says one, "A cat is worth as much to a farmer as his best hog or even his cow or horse, for the amount of grain one rat will destroy in a year is enormous." In California and the Middle West cats formerly were the ranchers' only hope, eighteen or twenty being commonly kept on a single ranch to catch gophers and ground squirrels which were highly destructive of the grain. It is estimated that the brown house rat kills more chickens than any other animal, and to the chicken farmer, therefore, the cat is of value.

Enemies of the cat have argued that hawks, owls, minks, and weasels destroy ten or twelve mice to every one taken

*Moles, which are not rodents, are carnivorous and never eat vegetation, but they meet with objection in gardens because of the earthworks they throw up in tunneling their runways.

by house cats. Quite naturally this is true, since mice number thousands more in the woods and fields where these birds and animals get their prey than in the house or barn, and they must catch them to live. Mivart estimated that a cat's capacity for catching and swallowing mice is twenty a day, seven thousand three hundred a year. Many cats have been seen with a mouse in the mouth and one under each fore foot, and one cat has been known to capture eight rats in a single night. Some cats never care to hunt either rodents or birds, but the feline odor is so effective that Mivart observed that the number of rodents its presence puts to flight "is far in excess of the cat's destructive energy."

Doctor A. Buchanan, who was stationed as a Civil Surgeon in India, observed that the houses with the most cats were the ones the plague passed by, and expressed the opinion (1908) that "when the number is sufficient, the risk of plagues is abolished." He said that a strong tradition exists in the east in favor of keeping cats. The Indian rat is small, and a cat sometimes is seen with four dead ones in its mouth at once.

A rat is so fierce a fighter that despite its small size most men fear to corner it. With no weapons other than bare hands, they have come off ingloriously in a battle with one of these rodents; but the cat, without hesitation, tackles a rodent one-third and in some cases more than half its own size. It stuns the rat with a blow, then seizes it by the head in a vicelike grip which sometimes causes the eyes to drop from their sockets. After the combat only its head shows injury. Following an exceptionally hot fight we have seen a cat pant for three hours, with a scratched nose and blood on its breast. Too exhausted to eat, it sometimes lies down and sleeps before treating itself to half the rat; then it rests and sleeps again before taking the remainder. When we talk glibly of a cat catching a rat, we do not reflect what the victory cost our invincible little feline.

The cat is to be considered not only as an animal, a personality, an erstwhile god, and a valuable ally of civilized man, but as a long-standing source of valuable commercial products, because of its utilization in medicine, biology, as food, and for its fur and its fat.

THE CAT IN MEDICINE

In many countries the wild cat and later the domestic cat has been utilized in medicine. Edward Topsell, in 1658,* said that the "virtues of the wild kind are more effectual than the tame"; that the liver, dried and powdered, was good for stone, the fat for tumors, "gowt" and lameness; that the flesh, salted and sweetened, had power to draw wens from the body, and if warmed would cure hemorrhoids and pains in the back. The blood and fat were used for erysipelas, and the skins, worn with the fur turned under, were believed to give strength to the limbs. "When a man is raving in a fever," says an English proverb of 1721, "the cat cast over him will cure him." It was also believed that a salve made from cats' eyes would enable a person to see in the dark.

The bones and hair were used in medicine in China. In Europe, Champfleury relates that early in the nineteenth century "apothecaries sold a substance which pretended to be the grease of the wild cat for the cure of abscess, rheuma-

The History of Four-Footed Beastes and Serpents.

tism and ankylosis, under the title of *Axungia cati sylvestris*." (Seneca Indian doctors used the fat, blood, and excrement of the lynx as a cure for baldness, gout, and other ills.)

THE CAT IN BIOLOGY

Students of biology in the United States learn their anatomy by dissecting a cat or a rabbit, the cat being preferred because it is more readily procured and its anatomy more closely resembles man's. Dealers frequently furnish the cats already chloroformed and prepared, but if obtained alive the students chloroform and prepare them, the arteries being injected after death. In some cities colleges receive gas-killed cats from the police department.

THE CAT AS FOOD

The flesh of the wild cat is said to be firmer and sweeter than that of the domestic cat, and where wild cats abounded they were reserved for the consumption of the well-to-do, while the flesh of the domestic cat was relegated to the poor. In the seventeenth century the flesh of the tame cat, according to Topsell, was eaten in Spain and Germany. He said it was "sweet as a cony." Much later it was served as rabbit in France and England after the removal of head and tail.

An article in *Chambers Journal* of 1875 states that at that time cats were eaten in Asia and that in France the skins were sold to furriers, the fat to frying houses, and the flesh to low eating houses. According to Philip G. Hamerton the flesh was eaten in Paris in 1884.

The Chinese believed that if a child were fed with cat broth it never would be afflicted by tumors, though the same superstition has existed with regard to other animals. In 1838, according to one record, cats were fattened in cages, then served up in stews and considered a rare and savory dish. Champfleury says that in his day (he died in 1889) cats were served in China as cats and in France as rabbits. In England they were eaten, it is said, as late as 1899 and held more dainty than rabbit or pork, and an account in the English journal, *Our Cats,* records that they were relished in northern Italy in 1906, roasted with onions, garlic, parsley, bay leaf, red wine, and fragrant herbs. The *Cat Courier* states that cats were eaten in Spain in 1917.

An old English proverb runs, "A piece of a kid is worth two of a cat," but although this is said to refer to the flesh, it may be that only the hide was intended.

THE FUR OF THE CAT

For centuries the skins of cats, wild and tame, have been processed for fur. As it is written in the ancient Chinese classics,

> They take badgers, foxes and wild cats
> To make furs for our young princes.

In warm climates animals grow a thin coat which is not durable, the fur of those inhabiting colder regions therefore being more highly valued, and skins of domestic cats bred in the temperate zone were priced so low in former times that monks and nuns were permitted to wear no others, the cheap ones denoting humility.

We have mentioned the use of cat fur in France in 1875.

In 1895 Lydekker said the "skins are used extensively for coat linings, muffs, trimmings and rugs," and the colors generally were white, black, blue, and tabby. Black cats from Holland were in large demand, and he says also that 3000 were imported into England from America, their value being from three pence to eighteen pence a skin. In Angora the fur of the local long-haired cat was prized as an article of commerce in 1906. An anonymous article in *Harper's Weekly,* January 8, 1910, states that cats then were bred in Holland as fur-bearing animals. In London, as late as 1915, if a loved cat disappeared it was suspected that it had been stolen for its fur, and long prior to that time cat-stealing was a trade in France and England.*

In 1928 the coat of a domestic cat in the United States was worth from twelve cents to sixty-two cents, still the cheapest of skins. (The coat of the Canada lynx was worth from $7.00 to $21.50.)

Rendering companies inform us that at the present time cat skins are not removed when the carcases are rendered, because they are without value, and editors of fur trade journals advise us that skins of cats asphyxiated by humane societies are of small use in the fur industry, nor are they useful for felt; that no cat skin is of value unless taken during the winter months, and the fur is not popular except on cheap garments, rabbit fur being much more abundant and more suitable for general use:

There are certain methods and practises in the fur trade regarding the manner in which the cat skins are taken from the animals,

*In the United States cat-stealing occurs in the interests of vivisection. The thieves frequently are brought to justice, but those who knowingly receive stolen goods thus far have evaded the law.

scraped, cleaned, stretched and dried, and unless these methods are followed out the skins are of little value.

But according to this authority, *Fur Trade Review,* "There is a large business in cat skins here and in Europe," and the *American Fur Designer* tells us that "About 50,000 skins [of ordinary house cats] are used annually for trimming children's coats."

Mr. Max Bachrach, eminent New York fur consultant, gives us the following information:

From 1884 to date [1936] only a very small percentage of domestic cats has been used for fur purposes. We have at various times imported from Europe and elsewhere so-called house-cats, but these usually are a breed that have returned to the wild state. There are two important reasons why we do not use the domestic cat's peltry. First, it is not sufficiently good in quality to warrant its use, and secondly, the health laws in most places are very strict about its use after having been taken from asphyxiating sources. The cost of supplying these also, if all other features are agreeable, is higher than we would have to pay for much finer types of animal peltries.

Various papers in *The Japan Magazine* state that cat skins are used to cover the samisen, the three-stringed guitar of the Japanese geisha girls (snake skins having formerly been employed). These girls themselves are called Cats because of their grace and blandishments. At no time in history have the intestines of the cat (or any other small animal) been used in the manufacture of the substance known as catgut, which, since time immemorial, has been derived from the intestines of large animals such as sheep, first for musical strings and latterly also for surgical sutures, the latter now being made from the submucous layer of the small intestine of government-inspected sheep.*

THE FAT OF THE CAT

In Gottfried Keller's classic story of a century ago, *The Fat of the Cat,* it is averred that it was necessary for the cat voluntarily to yield its fat; and the cat in his tale was quite too clever to be fooled into giving his life away.

We have mentioned that the fat of the domestic cat was sold to frying houses in France in 1875 and that earlier and later it was employed in medicine. In the present day it finds a new use. The bodies of hundreds of thousands of cats (and dogs) which are put to death by the various humane societies in the United States annually, when not incinerated are delivered to rendering companies, which ex-

---

*"The wilder the sheep the tougher the gut," is an expression familiar to musical instrument manufacturers.

"Some strings are being made from the intestines of hogs, and except for manufacturing difficulties the intestines of cows could also be used. Sheep gut is used primarily because of its length, texture and strength, and also because of the large number of sheep that are slaughtered annually. While deer intestines might be used, the quantity is extremely limited. There would not be enough felines in the world to make all the musical strings that are manufactured yearly." (Kaplan Musical String Company to the author.)

The term "catgut" is believed to be a misusage of "kitgut" or "kitstring," the old English word "kit" meaning a dancing master's fiddle.

"It is probable that at some time 'kit' was misconstrued as 'kitten,' thus conveying the meaning of a young cat, and thence the word 'catgut.' The catgut suture evolved from the musical string. Twisted intestines of sheep were used to make the strings of the old Greek harps, and Rhazes (900 A.D.), the Arabian surgeon, is credited with having been the first to stitch abdominal wounds with such harp strings." (Quoted by permission from *Manual of Surgical Sutures and Ligatures,* published by Davis & Geck, Inc.)

tract the grease, the residue forming a base for fertilizer.*
The grease is blended with other grease and distilled to
produce red-oil and stearic acid. Red-oil is used for oiling
wool after it has been "scoured" and made harsh, so that
the wool will spin freely with yarn, and is extracted from
the finished goods by washing with a potash red-oil soap.
Stearic acid after decomposition is separated from the red-
oil by pressure and used in the manufacture of soaps and
candles, its glycerine content being refined and sold as such.

It will be seen, therefore, that the candle-loving mouse
eventually may devour the cat.

*Bodies of horses and condemned cattle and hogs also are rendered
together and the grease used in soap-making and in the manufacture
of some shoe polishes.

Chapter Nineteen

CAT AND CHILD, AND CAT AND OLD MAN

CAT AND CHILD

CHILDREN treat dumb animals in the way they themselves are treated at home. If beaten they retaliate by beating the animals. The gratifying change which has come over children in recent years, particularly boys, in their attitude toward cats is due in part to instruction in the schools and newspaper and radio publicity given the cat, but chiefly to the improved methods of dealing with boys at home, which have brought about a better understanding of child psychology, and the work of psychiatrists in the instruction of mothers. It is remarkable also how the cat has prospered under this friendly attitude of the child and how its timidity and distrust are disappearing. To those who have witnessed this change it is a pleasure to walk along a city street and see a boy of ten years stoop to speak to a cat and stroke it gently, and to find an apartment house lad taking his dog and cat out together on leashes.

Says Compton Mackenzie, "Every normal child prefers a cat to a puppy, the reason for which may often be a recognition of a richer personality—a personality nearer to its human self."

Often the cat is the first creature from which a child gains the knowledge of its kinship with the animal world, and the cat is exceedingly devoted to children who are gentle and affectionate, and loves to play with them. Mr. Thomas H. Howley informs us that when a family cat that was fond of his two-year-old brother wanted the child to play with it, it seated the boy on the floor by placing a paw on each of his shoulders. (See also p. 147.)

The presence of any pet in the house exerts a moral and educational influence on children, and a full-grown cat rarely scratches a child. People have told us that their cat would allow the baby to maul it but would not permit any other member of the family to do so.

Doctor Cadwalader C. Vinton writes us:

In Korea thirty years ago my niece, who was visiting us there, had a large tom cat named Nicodemus. One day my youngest son, then aged seven, was heard to break out crying in such agony as to draw all of us running to the verandah where he had been building a block house. The structure was in ruins, the cat knocking the blocks about, and his plea was, "Papa, make Nicodemus stop teasing me."

Mr. Herbert C. Sprague of Brockton, Massachusetts, writes us:

My sister's little boy has a cat named Snooks, who travels with the boy, on his back, and will hardly let him out of sight. It waits for the boy to come home from school and will not eat anything unless the boy gives it to it himself. It is not a prize or pedigreed cat, just plain cat.

Hall and Browne, after considerable study of the subject, concluded that "Children perceive the cat's fondness for people," and that "The care of a pet tends to develop a sense of responsibility in a child and a humane consideration for other animals."

"Every normal child prefers a cat to a puppy," says Compton
Mackenzie. The children are Jean and David Utter,
cousins, of Georgetown, N. Y.

THE OLD MAN AND HIS CATS

Many men who never noticed cats during their active business life
devote a large part of their late leisure to these animals.

In the care of a cat a child learns to be just and unselfish, and if required to contribute to the cat's welfare, will learn thrift. If the child is obliged to care for the cat at certain hours, this is an excellent training in punctuality and kindliness.

Dorothy Canfield Fisher considers that "Cats are a necessary element in every child's life as examples (inspiriting to children hard beset by adults as they are) of how to live with creatures physically more powerful and yet preserve self-respect and dignity."

CAT AND OLD MAN

Men frequently turn to the soothing feline for comfort in their declining years, and many who never noticed cats during their active business life devote a large part of their late leisure to these animals. An uncle of the author who spent many energetic years in business paid very little attention to the family cats until after his retirement, when he became greatly attached to them. When he sat in his Morris chair of an evening a young brown cat usually reposed on his spacious chest, and with whatsoever topic the conversation began, it was certain to conclude with a dissertation on cats.

Through Miss Linda M. French we have received from Miss Anna M. Cole of Hampton, New Hampshire, the following illustration of the speed with which an elderly man is won over to a cat, even though it is of a color which he dislikes:

Father liked black cats and when you suggested giving me a white kitten, I spoke of it to him. "No, I don't want a white cat around here!" was most emphatically said. Nevertheless the kitten was such a darling, I let you persuade me to bring him home. Father did not say much, but I could see he was thoroughly displeased. The kitten understood how things stood and there was no yowling. He modestly effaced himself, sat down at a distance and washed his face, took a nap behind the door, purred and rubbed against me, not Father, who presently was watching out of the corner of his eye. The next day he announced, "We will call him Snowball," and was much pleased when the kitten tagged him about, sometimes going to the field when he hoed and waiting around to come back with him.

Robert P. Tristram Coffin understood the strong friendship which seems to be inherent between an old man and a cat when he wrote of the ancient clam digger, "Lonelier than a whippoorwill," who "never kept as much as hens," but "Naturally, he had some cats."

Chapter Twenty

AILUROPHOBES, CAT HATERS,
AND CAT LOVERS

AILUROPHOBES

AN AILUROPHOBE, as defined by psychiatric science, is not a cat hater, as commonly believed, but a person who dreads and fears cats. The origin of this singular word is not without interest, for it appears to have begun with Herodotus, the Greek historian (fifth century B.C.), who, on first meeting cats in Egypt, called them *ailuroi*—tail wavers; but the New York *Bookman* is credited with having been the first to use the word *ailurophobia,* from the Greek *ailuros* (cat) and *phobos* (fear). Rendered *phobia,* we are familiar with this latter word as a suffix to many words—hydrophobia (fear of water); cynophobia (fear of dogs); ophiophobia (fear of snakes, the commonest of the phobias); zoophobia (fear of animals); ailurophobia (fear of cats), etc.

Most, if not all these animal fears are induced in childhood either by fright or by the foolish example or ignorance of adults; but we have one exceptional case where cat fear was caused by the cat itself. Says Miss Leora Wilson:

To be perfectly frank, Bob is the first cat I ever liked. I imagine that this was because my paternal grandmother had a huge pure white tom cat called Dandy Jim from Caroline, who seemed to be intensely jealous of their attentions to me, their first grandchild. It was their custom to place me in the top box that covered their sewing machine, which had been set on the floor, and give me bread and butter and brown sugar to eat. Dandy Jim would walk up and give me a slap on the cheek, and when I cried and dropped the bread, take it away. This happened when I was creeping and trying to walk, and up until I was seven or so I would be so frightened at the sight of a cat that I nearly fainted. Once I did faint when the door was locked and I was unable to get away from the cat. My mother found me unconscious on the porch floor when she came in answer to my screams.

Miss G. Florence Janes of Brooklyn, New York, tells us that in childhood she was so terrified by the presence of a cat that if only the tablecloth touched her legs she became nervous. She recalls that once she was shut in a closet with a cat and was in great fear of it, but cannot remember how her ailurophobia began. Like Miss Wilson she made a complete recovery, though she "cannot enthuse about cats."

In some ailurophobes the horror is of a mild nature. They fear to touch cats but are kind to the animals, feeding them and letting them in and out of the house. Some know when there is a cat in the room even though it is hidden from view. Others are so violently distressed as to change color if a cat is mentioned.

The very presence of a cat in the house with General Sir Frederick Roberts is said to have given him asthma. Joseph Bonaparte, once King of Naples and Spain, while stopping with his retinue at Saratoga Springs, New York, in 1825, was given a dinner party by Mr. Henry Walton, which he attended with his sister and two daughters. He grew suddenly pale, while perspiration broke out on his forehead, and turning to his host, gasped, "Un chat! Un chat!" Mr. Walton instructed a waiter to remove the cat. No cat was in sight, but a search revealed a kitten under the sideboard.

The agitated guest is said to have suffered several hours' complete prostration. Napoleon also is numbered in the list of famous ailurophobes. Henry III, voluptuous and superstitious, kept 2000 lap dogs but fainted at sight of a cat. Others have gone into convulsions, suffered from temporary blindness, from nausea similar to seasickness, and even from lockjaw.

Many of these extreme cases, beginning in childhood, are continued through life by superstitious and exaggerated notions of the cat's occult properties, added to the fact that cats appear to delight in the company of some ailurophobes and pester them with attentions. For this strange feline conduct there is no explanation unless it be that cats have such a keen sense of humor that this is perhaps their way of laughing at people who are foolish enough to be afraid of them.

A competent psychiatrist usually can dispel a phobia.

CAT HATERS

The domestic feline has numbered many celebrated haters, though few have left a statement concerning the reason for their antipathy to the animal. It is noteworthy that the vigor with which they have maligned it and their zeal in defaming its reputation have been matched only by the ardor of many cat lovers in expressing their infatuation for the creature and their eagerness to see it perched on a pedestal for universal admiration.

Contrary to popular belief, all literati have not loved cats. Buffon hated them so bitterly that he could not tell the truth about them; Maeterlinck's cat is "a libel" in the opinion of the noted cat lover, Frank Swinnerton; Oliver Goldsmith is said to have abhorred cats, and Boswell's hatred of the animals prevented him from learning the details, which would have been priceless to all cat lovers, concerning the several felines Doctor Johnson told him he had owned previous to his acquisition of Hodge.

Cat enthusiasts seek to prove that Shakespeare loved cats by quoting "Care killed a cat" (*Much Ado About Nothing*) and the reference to "the harmless necessary cat" in *The Merchant of Venice;* but unhappily the majority of Shakespeare's allusions to cats are vilifications. An example:

> I could endure anything but a cat
> And now he's a cat to me. . . .
> A pox upon him! For he is more and more a cat.
> —*All's Well that Ends Well*

The inimitable bard is entitled to a place among the cat haters. If he loved cats, he never wrote the plays. If Bacon loved cats, he never wrote them, for even in play so large a number of animadversions could hardly have been indulged in by a cat lover. Thus another angle is presented from which industrious investigators may endeavor to solve the baffling question of their authorship. Did Shakespeare and Bacon love cats, and did Beaumont and Fletcher hate them? What was the attitude of Rutland, William Stanley, Edward de Vere, and Shapleigh toward cats?

Incredible though it may seem, Henry Bergh, who founded the Bergh Society in New York, which later became the American Society for the Prevention of Cruelty to Animals, is recorded in various contemporary references as a cat hater who desired the extermination of all cats. His society was organized in the interest of horses and cattle, though it now specializes mainly in cats and dogs.

The American Medical Association in its publications frequently has condemned the cat as a carrier of disease, and any statement to that effect is biased, since the cat is no more guilty than the human being, if as much so; nor is it just to condemn the cat more strongly than any other furry pet as a companion for a child ill with a contagious disease. Dogs naturally carry many more dangerous diseases than cats, and rabbits, guinea pigs, monkeys, white mice, white rats, and all other furry creatures will harbor a contagious disease quite as readily as a cat. It is profitable to reflect that the kiss of a healthy cat is safe, that of a human being is not.

A favorite argument of cat haters is that cats are responsible for the loss of some vegetation because of their destruction of birds which eat insects that destroy the crops. Walt Mason went so far as to say that this results in high prices for bread which people cannot pay and therefore go to the poorhouse or the morgue on account of the cat! (Perhaps he was joking.) An enormous amount of vegetation is destroyed by dogs and the Department of Agriculture recommends, not trapping and killing the dogs as in the case of the cats (the government furnishes free instructions for making cat traps), but spraying with nicotine sulphate all valuable trees, bushes, and shrubs to keep the dogs away.

Cat haters in America have the ear not only of the Federal Government, but of some state governments, that of New York, for example, where the Conservation Law provides that licensed hunters, trappers, and fishers may "humanely destroy a cat at large found hunting or killing any bird protected by law or with a dead bird of any species protected by law in its possession, and no action for damages shall be maintained for such killing"; and "sportsmen," looking upon the cat as a rival and with the state behind them, boast even in the press of killing every cat they meet. (With characteristic human inconsistency the law fails to provide that men found hunting or killing protected birds and animals, such as pheasants and deer, may be humanely shot by the game warden or peace officer, without redress from relatives.)

A Cat Exterminating Society was founded in New York City a few years ago, but we are informed that it passed out of existence for want of support.

One of the most violent cat haters of all time was a Chicago banker named Rockwell Sayre, who dreamed of ridding the world of cats by 1925, giving as his reasons that they are "filthy and useless," they "catch birds and spread disease," and that it is "toadying to depravity to keep a cat around the house." He gave small rewards to cat killers, ten cents each for the first 100, offered "$100 to the person who killed the last nasty cat on earth," had for his slogan, "A catless world quick," and circulated some verses which began,

> Who kills a Cat gains a year,
> Who kills a hundred never dies.

He claimed that 7,000,000 cats were destroyed during the first ninety days of his campaign, but having failed to annihilate the world's feline population by 1925, he promised that in another ten years not one cat would remain on earth. In a letter to the author (January 26, 1925) this man said, "We thank heaven more and more every day that we were allowed a presence and mission in this world." Although by his own maxim entitled to live forever, Rockwell

Sayre's presence was withdrawn from this feline-inhabited globe before the decade had passed and his "heavenly" mission ended.

CAT LOVERS

The Arabs say, "The cat was given to Adam and Eve for comfort when they went out into the desert alone," and it might be added that most cat lovers are those who believe in an exchange of comforts between the cat and themselves. Many attempts have been made to narrow into some specific groove the types of mind that are attracted to the small feline, but they have proved unsuccessful. Some cat lovers make extravagant statements: that only high intelligences love the cat, that no bad man ever loved a cat, and so on. (This is similar to saying, as they do, that there is no such thing as a stupid cat. See p. 118.)

Frank Swinnerton says, "The cat is for those who care for the subtle intimacies of the spirit." Perhaps this is a fair generalization, as it comprises persons of all ages and races, following every occupation, and with every degree of intelligence.

Among workers with their hands and with their heads we find individuals who feel that home is not complete unless a cat shares the broad comforts of the fireside. Dissimilar to these are dreamers and mystics who entertain so strong a passion for cats as cats that although the creatures do not thrive with crowding, they maintain dozens of them in restricted quarters.

Many eminent people—presidents, philosophers, musicians, legislators, scientists, and others—have immortalized their favorite cats, singly or jointly, directly or indirectly.

In the celebrated portrait of George Washington kneeling

beside his mother's chair, a cat is pictured in the background in deference to our first President's reputed fondness for these animals. Well authenticated reports prove that Abraham Lincoln entertained a tender affection for cats. Jacob Riis said that when Theodore Roosevelt was leading to dinner a train of distinguished guests at the White House, he turned aside on finding Slippers, the White House cat, lying in his path, and the entire company turned aside also. As soon as the President had seated the lady he was escorting, he excused himself, and before the guests had all passed into the dining room, picked up the cat lest some servant punish it and carried it to a safe place. Slippers is said to have been a gray cat with double paws. (See also p. 145.)

Fontenelle, the French philosopher, for more than forty years widely noted for his oratorical gifts, had a cat on which he liked to try his speeches, and seating it in an armchair, delivered them to it. This spirit of youthfulness, it has been hinted, may have helped the philosopher to attain his hundredth year.

"The Cat of St. James," a celebrated English feline described by Charles Larcom Graves,* was loved by many musicians and Lady Burdett Coutts presented him with his collar. When Paderewski gave his first recital at St. James with only 100 persons in the hall, he said to the cat, "Wish me good luck," whereupon the obliging creature jumped on his lap and purred; and after the concert Paderewski played *The Cat's Fugue* for him in the artists' room.

Between Jeremy Bentham, who lived much alone, and Sir Samuel Romilly a close friendship existed which Bentham is said to have explained by saying that the love for pussies was

Diversions of a Music Lover, 1904.

Photograph by William Henry

A celebrated cat lover was Leon Barritt, the astronomer, who, with Garrett P. Serviss, invented a planisphere.

Truman T. Pierson, humanitarian, is one of the founders of
the Allied Cat Lovers, Inc.

their bond of union. Romilly, he is quoted as saying, "kept a noble puss, and I never failed to pay it my respects."

Peg Woffington, calling on Christopher Rich, the manager of Covent Garden, found him ensconced on a sofa in the midst of twenty-seven cats.* Two dozen Angoras kept by the eminent sociologist, Vilfredo Pareto, were so sacred in his eyes that he seldom permitted visitors to see them,† but in numbers he and Rich apparently were outstripped by Charles Paul de Kock, French novelist and dramatist, who is reputed to have kept thirty cats. *Chambers Journal* of March, 1872, relates that a Mrs. Griggs of Southampton Road, who died in 1792, left eighty-six living cats and twenty-eight dead ones, and her will provided £150 a year for the maintenance of her black servant and the cats. Hamerton says the dead cats were mounted in glass cases and that Mrs. Griggs lived in Edinburgh. The record number of cats maintained by one person, however, appears to have been reached by Mrs. Kate Johnson of San Francisco, with 350 long-haired cats, 42 of which are portrayed by Carl Kahler in "My Wife's Lovers," which is called "the world's greatest painting of cats." The legend attached to copies of the painting states that Mrs. Johnson eventually bequeathed half a million dollars for the care of her cats.‡

Woffington. A Tribute to the Actress and the Woman, by Augustin Daly, 1888.

†"Pareto as I Knew Him," by M. M. Einaudi, *Atlantic Monthly,* Sept., 1935.

‡Many people have left legacies to their cats. ("Die and endow a college or a cat."—Alexander Pope.) In the United States two cats each received a legacy of $5000 during the year 1939, one, Tommy Tucker, in New York City, whose owner was Miss Louise Baier, and the other, Lilly, in Sacramento, California, who had been owned by Miss Annie Hansche.

From long familiarity with his favorite pets, Chateaubriand, noted French author and statesman, likened himself to a cat, and one biography of Gottfried Mind avers that when he died in 1814 his features had acquired a feline aspect from close association with cats to the exclusion of people; but in the case of many famous people it has been observed that the cat reflects the character of master or mistress. Chanoine, Victor Hugo's favorite cat, described as having had a huge ruff of white fur and "whiskers like those of a Hungarian Magyar," had the habit of seating itself on a large red ottoman in the center of the grand salon, "awaiting the homage of visitors with grave dignity," or leaving its cushion and solemnly advancing to meet the visitors, causing them to realize the truth of the saying, "In a learned house even the cat is learned." This lordly animal is said also to have prompted people to repeat the famous remark of Joseph Méry, the French satirist: "God made the cat that man might have the pleasurable sense of caressing the tiger."

Many a noble master has been enslaved by his cat. Beside him when he wrote, Charles Dickens' deaf cat would sit, often putting out the candle to compel him to pay attention to her; and Julian Hawthorne's cat, Tom, who sat on his shoulder as he wrote, jumped down on the table when he thought his master had done enough for one sitting, and pulled away the manuscript. Cardinal Wolsey so respected his cat that he is said to have "accommodated it with part of his regal seat when he gave an audience or received princely company," and Théophile Gautier honored one of his cats with the name of Madame Théophile. (The names people give their cats are not the least significant illustration of the effect cats have upon them.)

Leigh Hunt believed the reason Doctor Johnson went out

himself to buy oysters for Hodge when the cat was ailing was that his black servant was too proud to go. (Oysters were exceedingly cheap at that time and he probably bought only a penny's worth.)

Sarah B. Wister relates that her cat, Princess, was in the habit of rearing on her hind legs, pressing her nose against the face of her master or mistress, and patting them on the cheek with her forepaw; but she reserved this caress exclusively for them except on one occasion, when she bestowed it on a distinguished cat-loving visitor, Henry James.

The loved cat of Petrarch was embalmed and mummified by its bereaved master, in Egyptian fashion, and encased above the door of his study in the valley of Vaucluse.

The widow of Benjamin Constant stated that on a certain day her husband was expected to make an important speech in the Chamber of Deputies but failed to appear, and his friends, going to his home, found him in his study quietly reading. When told that everybody was waiting, he answered, "What can I do? Look here! There's my cat sleeping in the center of the papers I have prepared for my speech, and until she wakes, how can I drag her off?" (This cat was an Angora.)

Leon Barritt, the noted astronomer who, with Garrett P. Serviss, invented a planisphere and who was editor of *The Monthly Evening Sky Map,* had his portrait made with his handsome black-and-white cat on his lap. Mr. A. A. Steward, a cat lover of England, in 1925 founded a notable institution, The Cats' Protection League, and Messrs. Truman T. Pierson and Charles A. Johnson, cat lovers of America, in 1939 founded a somewhat similar organization, the Allied Cat Lovers, Inc.

It is well known that Southey dated his letters "Cats' Eden," and that France's great minister, Jean Baptiste Colbert, founder of the Academy of Sciences and other institutions of art and learning, felt himself unable to work without one or two cats on his table, and said that when they began to purr his thoughts began to flow. Pierre Loti is said to have provided his cats with visiting cards, and among other eminent people who have loved cats are included Matthew Arnold, Thomas Henry Huxley, Walter Pater, Anatole France, Thomas Hood, Andrew Lang, Mary E. Wilkins Freeman, Ella Wheeler Wilcox, Sarah Orne Jewett, Walter Savage Landor, Emile Zola, Victorien Sardou, and Lafcadio Hearn who said, "Very much do I love cats." Other celebrities named as admirers of the domestic feline are Einstein, Yehudi Menuhin, Fannie Hurst, Paul Honoré, Clemenceau, Julia Marlowe, Irene Castle McLaughlin, Sheila Kaye-Smith, George H. H. H. Clisbee, Booth Tarkington, William Lyon Phelps, Thomas Hardy, Thomas Gray, Claude Bragdon, Louis Untermeyer, Poincaré, and Lenin.*

Thomas Hardy wrote of his cat, "Pet was never mourned as you," and testimonials to the deep affection of thousands of sorrowing owners of these small, insinuating quadrupeds exist in the graves of their pets, world over, some marked

*The omission of Mark Twain from this list will be noticed by all who have read other lists of outstanding cat lovers. Mark Twain had a kindly heart and he penned a vehement protest against vivisection, for which all animal lovers must feel eternally grateful, but there is nothing in his writings or personal associations with domestic felines which warrants his inclusion in a list of cat lovers. We all have a blind spot in the eye and a stupid spot in the brain, and Mark Twain's stupid spot appears to have been cats. See "Mark Twain's Pets," by Edwin Wildman, *St. Nicholas*, Jan., 1899, and "Mark Twain and the Cat." by Herman Spencer, *Harper's Weekly*, Feb. 9, 1907.

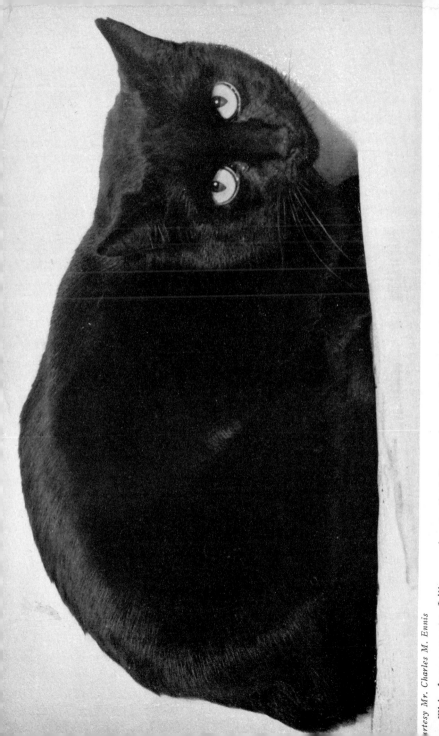

This fortunate cat, Lilly, was bequeathed $5,000 in 1939 by her late owner, Miss Annie Hansche of Sacramento, Calif.

A victim of misplaced maternal instinct, this cat, Baby, had never been permitted to walk and was unable to stand.

with elaborately inscribed monuments, some with sculptured urns or sundials.

MISPLACED MATERNAL INSTINCT

The cat normally takes the place of a child with many lonely men and women and also with childless couples, who frequently maintain a number of cats. In abnormal cases a certain misplaced maternal instinct comes into play and a cat is enthroned as the baby of the household. Some years ago the author witnessed an example of this in a woman whose baby (she referred to it as such) was a fine large cat, snow white with green eyes, which she attired in human infant's garments and carried about indoors and out, precisely like a child in long clothes. In street-cars it wore a bonnet with a white veil over its face. The animal growled when touched and was unable to stand. It never had been permitted to walk.

DECLINE AND RISE OF STATUS IN MODERN TIMES

Had the cat never left the Orient the story of its past would be infinitely pleasanter, for though no longer actively worshiped after the destruction of Egyptian culture, it seldom has lost the esteem of Orientals. In Europe, however, it was destined to fall from the most exalted position of any animal in history to the most cruelly used. We have seen how the cat, prior to the nineteenth century, had suffered like the witch from human ignorance and religious superstition, which went so far as to constitute it a responsible moral agent in order to convict it of crimes far beyond its possibilities. It was even accused of hating blue, the alleged dress of the Virgin Mary, and the writings of Addison, De

Quincey, and others show that once the habit had been formed of persecuting the animal for the devil's sake, it continued in the name of "sport."

Except for man in the Inquisition, no creature passed through so horrible an ordeal, and its misery was particularly great in Germany, France, and England. Whether or not it was because the cat seemed human that man's inhumanity to man was extended to include this small being also, we do not know, but no animal, at the beginning of the nineteenth century possessed any rights in Europe. In 1809 Lord Thomas Erskine, who had a passion for espousing worthy but unpopular causes, read before the House of Lords his famous appeal for a Bill against Cruelty to Animals. By 1822 a bill had been passed against the ill-treatment of cattle, and in 1849 an act imposed a penalty for cruelty to any animal, the word to include dogs and cats as well as farm stock.

As education advanced in the latter half of the nineteenth century and the belief in devils and witches began to disappear, the rights of animals received increasing consideration, prominent zoophilists rose publicly to extol the cat's admirable qualities, and the general attitude gradually improved.

It has come about, therefore, that though cats formerly were wild animals in the eye of the law and belonged to nobody, they are held as property today in many countries and their owners are responsible for their well-being and happiness. Throughout the world, particularly in Germany, France, and England, the "fireside sphinx" is idolized and gently nurtured by countless thousands of enthusiastic cat lovers—a striking illustration of the theory that events move in cycles.

SELECTED BIBLIOGRAPHY

SELECTED BIBLIOGRAPHY*

CAT FAMILY

The Natural History of the Felinæ, William Jardine, 1834.

A Monograph of the Felidæ or, Family of the Cats, Daniel Giraud Elliot, 1883.

A Hand Book of the Carnivora, Part I. Cats, Civets and Mungooses, Richard Lydekker, 1895.

"Phylogeny of the Felidæ," W. D. Matthew, *Bull.* Am. Mus. Nat. Hist., v. 28, p. 289, Art. 26, 1910.

Vertebrate Palæontology, Alfred Sherwood Romer, 1933.

DISTRIBUTION OF THE DOMESTIC CAT

"The Abyssinian Cat," H. C. Brooke (pamphlet), 1929.

Chinese Cat: *The Chinese Repository* (Notices in Natural History, Art. IV), v. 7, p. 595, May, 1838–April, 1839.

"The Chinese Cat," T. Torrance, *Jnl.* of the North-China Branch of the Royal Asiatic Soc'y, v. 57, p. 113, 1926.

Modern Egyptian Cat: Stanley Smyth Flower, *Proc.* Zool. Soc. of London, p. 387, 1932 [re Felidæ].

"English Domestic Cats," R. I. Pocock, *Proc.* Zool Soc. of London, v. I, p. 143, 1907.

*The number of books, short stories, essays, and scientific and other papers that have been published on the subject of cats—in English, French, German, Swedish, Arabic, Latin, and other languages—is estimated at more than four thousand, this figure being suggested as a modest one by Mr. Clarence L. Madden of New Bern, North Carolina, whose collection of books on the domestic cat is believed to be the most extensive in existence.

Indian Cat: Curator's Report, Asiatic Soc. of Bengal, Calcutta, p. 441, Aug., 1856, E. Blyth.
Beast and Man in India, John Lockwood Kipling, 1891, [p. 315, Cats].
Japanese Cat: *Things Japanese,* Basil Hall Chamberlain, 1902 [Cats, p. 84].
"The Cat," K. Takakuwa, *The Japan Magazine,* Jan., 1928.
Paraguayan Cat: *Natural History of the Mammals of Paraguay* [in German], Johann Rudolph Rengger, 1830.

SCIENTIFIC PAPERS ON SIAMESE, TABBIES, AND TORTOISE-SHELLS

"Siamese, an Albinistic Color Variation in Cats," W. E. Castle, *American Naturalist,* v. 53, p. 265, 1919.
"Crosses with Siamese Cats," K. Tjebbes, *Jnl. of Genetics,* v. 14, p. 355, 1924.
"Temperature Effects on the Color of the Siamese Cat," N. A. and V. N. Iljin, *Jnl. of Heredity,* p. 309, July, 1930.
"Allelomorphism of Silver and Siamese Coat Variations in the Domestic Cat," Clyde E. Keeler and Virginia Cobb, *Jnl. of Heredity,* v. 24, No. 5, 1933.
"Siamese-Persian Cats, Clyde E. Keeler and Virginia Cobb, *Jnl. of Heredity,* v. 27, No. 9, Sept., 1936.
"Our Tabby Cats," R. I. Pocock, *Mendel Jnl.,* No. 2, p. 53, Feb., 1911.
"On the Inheritance of Tortoiseshell and Related Colours in Cats," L. Doncaster, *Proc.* Cambridge Philos. Soc'y, v. 13, p. 35, 1904.
"The Tortoise Shell Cat," Phineas W. Whiting, *American Naturalist,* v. 49, p. 518, 1915.
"Is the Fertile Tortoise-shell Tom Cat a Modified Female?" C. C. Little, *Jnl. of Genetics,* v. 10, p. 301, 1920.
"The Male Tortoise Shell Cat," Ruth C. Bamber, *Jnl. of Genetics,* v. 12, p. 209, 1922.
"The Tortoise Shell Cat," F. A. Hayes, *Jnl. of Heredity,* v. 14, p. 369, 1923.

MISCELLANEOUS PAPERS ON INHERITANCE
AND ANCESTRY

"On Sex-Limited Inheritance in Cats," L. Doncaster, *Jnl. of Genetics,* v. 3, p. 11, 1913.

"Inheritance of Coat Color in Cats," P. W. Whiting, *Jnl. of Experimental Zool.,* v. 25, p. 539, 1918.

"Inheritance of White-Spotting and Other Color Characters in Cats," Phineas W. Whiting, *American Naturalist,* v. 53, p. 473, 1919.

Mostly Mammals—Zoological Essays, R. Lydekker, 1903, Chap. The Pedigree of the Cat.

WILD TRAITS IN THE DOMESTIC CAT

Wild Traits in Tame Animals, Louis Robinson, 1897.

HOW LONG IT TAKES DOMESTIC CATS TO GO WILD

"The Permanence of the Domestic Instinct in the Cat," C. A. White, *Knowledge,* Apr. 11, 1884.

PHYSIOLOGY OF THE CAT

The Cat. An Introduction to the Study of Backboned Animals, Especially Mammals, St. George Mivart, 1881.

Anatomy of the Cat, Jacob Reighard and H. S. Jennings, 1902; [Revised edition, 1935].

An Elementary Treatment of the Theory of Spinning Tops and Gyroscopic Motion. *How a Falling Cat Turns Over,* Harold Crabtree, 1914.

"Color Blindness of Cats," J. C. DeVoss and Rose Ganson, *Jnl. of Animal Behavior,* v. 5, p. 115, 1915.

"Notes on the Falling Reflex of Cats," H. R. Muller and L. H. Weed, *Am. Jnl. of Physiol.,* p. 373, May 1, 1916.

Mammalian Anatomy with special reference to The Cat, Alvin Davison, 1923 [4th ed. revised by Frank A. Stromsten].

"Do Cats Sharpen Their Claws?" Ole N. de Weerdt, *Science,* Oct. 28, 1927.

PSYCHOLOGY OF THE CAT

Our Cats and All About Them, Harrison William Weir, 1889.

Pussy and Her Language, Marvin R. Clark, 1895.

"The Psychic Development of Young Animals and its Physical Correlation." II. The Cat, Wesley Mills (paper), 1895.

"Cats and Their Affections," Sarah B. Wister, *Temple Bar Magazine,* Dec., 1895–Jan., 1896.

Animal Intelligence, George J. Romanes, 1906, Chap XIV, The Cat.

"Do Cats Think?" W. H. Hudson, *Living Age,* v. 309, p. 704, June 18, 1921 (from the *Cornhill Magazine* for May, 1921).

The Modern Cat: Her Mind and Manners. An Introduction to Comparative Psychology, Georgina Ida Stickland Gates, 1928.

"Experimental Studies of Adaptive Behavior in Cats," Donald Keith Adams, Johns Hopkins Press, 1929, *Comp. Psych. Monographs,* v. 6, serial No. 27.

THE CAT AND THE OCCULT

Animal Ghosts, or: Animal Hauntings and the Hereafter. Chap. I, Cats, Elliott O'Donnell, 1913.

"The Psychic Significance of the Cat," Ethel C. Hargrove, *Occult Review,* v. 25, p. 337, 1917.

The Cat in the Mysteries of Religion and Magic, M. Oldfield Howey, 1931?

HABITS AND INSTINCTS

Chapters on Animals, Philip Gilbert Hamerton, 1884.

The Cat, Philip M. Rule, 1887 (with an Essay on Feline Instinct, by Bernard Perez).

"Do Kittens Instinctively Kill Mice?" R. M. Yerkes and D. Bloomfield, *Psychol. Bull.,* vii, p. 253, 1910.

"Homing Powers of the Cat," Francis H. Herrick, *Scientific Monthly,* XIV, 525, 1922.

"Cats as Fishermen," E. W. Gudger, *Natural History,* v. 25, p. 143, 1925.

UTILIZATION OF THE CAT

"Cats as Plague Preventers," A. Buchanan, *British Medical Jnl.*, v. 2, p. 1285, 1908.

Researches into Chinese Superstitions, Henry Doré, 1918 [Tr. by M. Kennelly], v. 5, Art. IX, The Cat.

CAT AND CHILD

"The Cat and the Child," G. Stanley Hall and C. E. Browne, *Pedagogical Seminary*, v. 11, 1904.

"Why I Like Cats Better than Dogs," Dorothy Canfield Fisher, *American Magazine*, p. 38, Sept., 1926.

CAT WORSHIPERS

Manners and Customs of the Ancient Egyptians, John Gardner Wilkinson, 1878.

"The Cats of Ancient Egypt," W. M. Conway, *English Illust. Mag.*, p. 251, Jan., 1890.

The Gods of the Egyptians, or Studies in Egyptian Mythology, E. A. Wallis Budge, 1904.

"Notes on Some Small Egyptian Figures of Cats," Neville Langton, *The Jnl. of Egyptian Archæology*, v. XXII, Part II, Dec., 1936.

"Further Notes on Some Egyptian Figures of Cats," N. Langton, *The Jnl. of Egyptian Archæology*, v. XXIV, Part I, June, 1938.

CATS OF DISTINCTION

Celebrated Cats, Constantina E. Brooks, 189?

My Litereray Zoo (p. 75), Kate Sanborn, 1896.

Murthy's Cattage: A Biographical Dictionary of Cats in Literature [and those owned by historical personages]. To the Memory of Murthy, a cat,* Howard Chapin, 1911.

*The reference in Chapin's Dictionary to King Hana and his cat, Bouhaki, widely acclaimed as the first cat in history whose name is known, derives from Champfleury. Every succeeding cat writer has taken them for granted, but neither the king nor the cat ever had actual existence. See Mellen, *All-Pets Mag.*, Feb., 1940, p. 16.

INDEX